SOLUTIONS OF
LAPLACE'S EQUATION

LIBRARY OF MATHEMATICS

edited by

WALTER LEDERMANN

D.S., Ph.D., F.R.S.Ed., Senior Lecturer in
Mathematics, University of Manchester.

SOLUTIONS OF
LAPLACE'S EQUATION

BY

D. R. BLAND

ROUTLEDGE AND KEGAN PAUL
LONDON

First published 1961
by Routledge & Kegan Paul Ltd
Broadway House, 68-74 Carter Lane
London, E.C.4

Printed in Great Britain
by Latimer, Trend & Co Ltd, Plymouth

Preface

THIS book is an introduction both to Laplace's equation and its solutions and to a general method of treating partial differential equations. Chapter 1 discusses vector fields and shows how Laplace's equation arises for steady fields which are irrotational and solenoidal. In the second chapter the method of separation of variables is introduced and used to reduce each partial differential equation, Laplace's equation in different co-ordinate systems, to three ordinary differential equations. Chapters 3 and 5 are concerned with the solutions of two of these ordinary differential equations, which lead to treatments of Bessel functions and Legendre polynomials. Chapters 4 and 6 show how such solutions are combined to solve particular problems. This general method of approach has been adopted because it can be applied to other scalar and vector fields arising in the physical sciences; special techniques applicable only to the solutions of Laplace's equation have been omitted. In particular generating functions have been relegated to exercises. After mastering the content of this book, the reader will have methods at his disposal to enable him to look for solutions of other partial differential equations.

The author would like to thank Dr. W. Ledermann for his criticism of the first draft of this book.

D. R. BLAND

The University,
   Manchester 13.

Contents

CONTENTS

CHAPTER ONE

Occurrence and Derivation of Laplace's Equation

---

1. SITUATIONS IN WHICH LAPLACE'S EQUATION ARISES

If a vector **v** can be associated with each point in a given space, then **v** is said to be a vector field. Two everyday examples are an electric field and a velocity field in a moving fluid. In an electric field, the electric intensity **E** at any point is a vector whose magnitude and direction are equal to the magnitude and direction of the force which would be exerted on a unit charge if it were placed at that point; generally the vector **E** varies from point to point. In a fluid the velocity **v** at any point is the velocity of the particle instantaneously situated at that point. Although in general vector fields are functions of time as well as of space, in this book we shall be concerned only with space dependence and we shall assume that all vector fields with which we deal are steady, i.e. they do not change with time.

We shall now restrict ourselves to special types of steady vector fields, namely those that are both irrotational and solenoidal. First let us explain the meaning of these terms. Consider a curve C in space and let P and Q be two neighbouring points on the curve. Let the vector $\overrightarrow{PQ}$ be d**s**. Let the vector field **v** at P be equal to **v**(P). Then we can form the scalar product **v**(P) . d**s**. We can form this product for all adjoining pairs of neighbouring points on the curve. Suppose the curve starts at A and ends at B. Then, adding together the scalar product from each pair of neighbouring points, we obtain Σ**v** . d**s** where, in each term of the sum, **v** is the field vector at the first of the two points and d**s** is

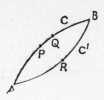

FIG. 1

the vector joining them. As ds→0, the number of terms in the sum becomes infinite and in the limit the sum becomes an integral. It is called the 'line integral' of **v** from A to B along the curve C and is denoted by

$$\int_{C}^{B}_{A} \mathbf{v} \cdot d\mathbf{s}.$$

In general the value of a line integral of a vector field between two points will depend on the path between them. The special property that distinguishes irrotational vector fields from other vector fields is simply that the value of the line integral of the vector field between any two points is independent of the path chosen between them. In the diagram above, this means that, if the curve C' had been chosen instead of C, then

$$\int_{C'}^{B}_{A} \mathbf{v} \cdot d\mathbf{s} = \int_{C}^{B}_{A} \mathbf{v} \cdot d\mathbf{s}. \tag{1}$$

The line integral of an irrotational vector field around any closed path is zero. This statement will now be proved.

FIG. 2

Suppose P, Q, R and S are any four points of the path. Then the integral around the closed path, denoted by $\oint$, can be split into two parts:

$$\oint \mathbf{v} \cdot d\mathbf{s} = \int_{\substack{P \\ \text{via } Q}}^{R} \mathbf{v} \cdot d\mathbf{s} + \int_{\substack{R \\ \text{via } S}}^{P} \mathbf{v} \cdot d\mathbf{s}.$$

Now

$$\int_{\substack{R \\ \text{via } S}}^{P} \mathbf{v} \cdot ds = - \int_{\substack{P \\ \text{via } S}}^{R} \mathbf{v} \cdot d\mathbf{s},$$

because interchanging the limits of an integral alters its sign. But, since $\mathbf{v}$ is irrotational,

$$\int_{\substack{P \\ \text{via } S}}^{R} \mathbf{v} \cdot d\mathbf{s} = \int_{\substack{P \\ \text{via } Q}}^{R} \mathbf{v} \cdot d\mathbf{s}.$$

Therefore

$$\oint \mathbf{v} \cdot d\mathbf{s} = 0.\dagger \tag{2}$$

Let us choose any fixed point O and associate with it the number $\phi(O)$. With any other point P, associate $\phi(P)$ where

$$\phi(P) = \phi(O) + \int_{O}^{P} \mathbf{v} \cdot d\mathbf{s}. \tag{3}$$

For an irrotational vector field, the line integral $\int_{O}^{P} \mathbf{v} \cdot d\mathbf{s}$ is independent of the path chosen and therefore only one number is associated with each point in space. When one number is associated with each point in space, these numbers form what is known as a 'scalar field'. Equation (3) shows that with any irrotational vector field a scalar field

---

† A general motion of a rigid body can be resolved into a translation without rotation and a rotation about any point. In the translation the motion of any point is represented by a constant vector, $\mathbf{a}$ say, and, therefore, for any path in the body

$$\oint \mathbf{a} \cdot d\mathbf{s} = \mathbf{a} \cdot \oint d\mathbf{s} = 0$$

because $\mathbf{s}$ returns to its original value at the end of the cycle. Since $\oint \mathbf{a} \cdot ds = 0$ for irrotational motion, the word 'irrotational' has come to be used for all vector fields which satisfy $\oint \mathbf{v} \cdot d\mathbf{s}$ over any closed path.

can be associated and that this scalar field is indeterminate to the extent of an arbitrary additive constant, $\phi(O)$.

Let us apply equation (3) to a point Q in the neighbourhood of P such that $\overrightarrow{PQ}=d\mathbf{s}$. Then

$$\phi(Q)=\phi(O)+\int_O^Q \mathbf{v} \cdot d\mathbf{s}.$$

On subtraction of equation (3) from the above equation,

$$\phi(Q)-\phi(P)=\int_P^Q \mathbf{v} \cdot d\mathbf{s}.$$

Since Q is in the neighbourhood of P, the integrand $\mathbf{v}$ in the integral $\int_P^Q \mathbf{v} \cdot d\mathbf{s}$ can be expanded by Taylor's theorem, as

$$\mathbf{v}=\mathbf{v}(P)+O(|d\mathbf{s}|),$$

where $O(|d\mathbf{s}|)$ is a term of the same order of magnitude as $d\mathbf{s}$. Therefore $\phi(Q)-\phi(P)=\mathbf{v}(P) \cdot d\mathbf{s}+O(|d\mathbf{s}|^2)$. Now the scalar product of $\mathbf{v}(P)$ and $d\mathbf{s}$ is equal to the product of the component of $\mathbf{v}(P)$ in the direction of $d\mathbf{s}$ times the magnitude of $d\mathbf{s}$. Denoting the component by $\{\mathbf{v}(P)\}_{d\mathbf{s}}$,

$$\phi(Q)-\phi(P)=\{\mathbf{v}(P)\}_{d\mathbf{s}} |d\mathbf{s}|+O(|d\mathbf{s}|^2),$$

or

$$\{\mathbf{v}(P)\}_{d\mathbf{s}}=\frac{\phi(Q)-\phi(P)}{|d\mathbf{s}|}+O(|d\mathbf{s}|).$$

Let $d\mathbf{s}\to 0$, then $\dfrac{\phi(Q)-\phi(P)}{|d\mathbf{s}|}$ tends to the derivative of ϕ with respect to distance in the direction along $d\mathbf{s}$, denoted by $\dfrac{\partial\phi}{\partial s}$, and

$$\{\mathbf{v}(P)\}_{d\mathbf{s}}=\frac{\partial\phi}{\partial s}, \tag{4}$$

i.e. *the component of an irrotational vector field in any direction at any point is equal to the space derivative of the associated scalar field in that direction at that point.*

We shall now consider the defining property of a solenoidal

4

vector field **v**. Let S be any closed surface in the space in which the vector field **v** is defined and consider a small element of this surface with area dS, whose outward normal is parallel to the unit vector **n**.

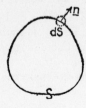

Form the scalar product **v . n** and multiply by dS. Repeat for every element of the surface and add to give $\sum$**v . n** dS. Let d$S \to 0$. The number of terms in the sum tends to infinity and the sum becomes the surface integral $\int_S$**v . n** dS. *A vector field is said to be solenoidal in any volume V, if for all closed surfaces S enclosing space entirely within the volume V,*

$$\int_S \mathbf{v} \cdot \mathbf{n}\, dS = 0. \tag{5}$$

The word 'solenoidal' is used because the electric field in the space within a solenoid satisfies equation (5).

As previously stated, attention is confined in this book to vector fields that are both irrotational and solenoidal, i.e. the vector fields satisfy both equations (4) and (5). Now the integrand of equation (5), **v . n**, is a scalar and is equal to the component of **v** in the direction of **n**. But by equation (4) the component of **v** in the direction of **n** is equal to $\dfrac{\partial \phi}{\partial n}$ where $\dfrac{\partial \phi}{\partial n}$ denotes the derivative of ϕ with respect to distance along the outward normal to the surface. Substituting **v . n** $= \dfrac{\partial \phi}{\partial n}$ into equation (5),

$$\int_S \frac{\partial \phi}{\partial n}\, dS = 0. \tag{6}$$

i.e. *the scalar field ϕ, associated with an irrotational vector field which is also solenoidal, satisfies the equation*

$$\int_s \frac{\partial \phi}{\partial n}\, \mathrm{d}S = 0.\dagger$$

Equation (6) is the integral form of Laplace's equation. It has different forms in different co-ordinate systems. These forms are partial differential equations and are found in sections 2 and 3 of this chapter.

Laplace's equation occurs whenever a steady vector field is irrotational and solenoidal. The gravitational and electrostatic fields in free space, except at points where there is mass or charge, and the velocity field in an incompressible irrotational fluid are examples of such fields. Let $\mathbf{F}$ be the force on unit mass in the gravitational field, let $\mathbf{E}$ be the force on unit charge in the electrostatic field and let $\mathbf{v}$ be the velocity of an incompressible irrotational fluid, then in all cases we can introduce a scalar field ϕ such that the component of the vector field at any point in the direction of $\mathrm{d}\mathbf{s}$ is given by

$$\{\mathbf{F}\}_{\mathrm{d}s} = \frac{\partial \phi}{\partial s}, \quad \{\mathbf{E}\}_{\mathrm{d}s} = \frac{\partial \phi}{\partial s} \text{ and } \{\mathbf{v}\}_{\mathrm{d}s} = \frac{\partial \phi}{\partial s}.$$

For gravitational and electric fields it is convenient to introduce $V = -\phi$. If the arbitrary constant occurring in ϕ is chosen so that $\phi = 0$ at infinity, then $V(P)$ is equal to the energy that would be released if unit mass (or unit positive charge) moved from P to infinity. This will now be proved. The energy released is equal to the work done by the external forces in moving unit mass (or charge) from infinity to P. These forces must be equal and opposite to the vector field forces. Therefore

---

† If a vector field is irrotational and solenoidal only in a particular part of space, then $\int_s \frac{\partial \phi}{\partial n} \mathrm{d}S = 0$ over all closed surfaces S drawn within that part of space. The integral is not in general zero for closed surfaces enclosing any space outside that part.

energy released $= -\int_{\infty}^{P} \mathbf{F} \cdot d\mathbf{s}$ or $-\int_{\infty}^{P} \mathbf{E} \cdot d\mathbf{s}$

$$= -\phi(P) + \phi(\infty) \text{ by equation (3)}$$
$$= V(P),$$

since $\phi = -V$ and $\phi(\infty) = 0$.

Substitution of $\phi = -V$ gives

$$\{\mathbf{F}\}_{ds} = -\frac{\partial V}{\partial s}, \quad \{\mathbf{E}\}_{ds} = -\frac{\partial V}{\partial s} \quad \text{and} \quad \{\mathbf{v}\}_{ds} = \frac{\partial \phi}{\partial s}. \quad (7)$$

V is called the potential of the gravitational or electrostatic field. ϕ is called the velocity potential of the velocity field. Henceforth we shall refer to the associated scalar field as the 'scalar potential' or just the 'potential' of the vector field. We shall employ ϕ when a positive sign is taken in deriving the vector field, V when a negative sign is to be inserted.

There are also applications of Laplace's equation where it is the scalar field ϕ, and not the vector field $\mathbf{v}$, which is the physically measurable quantity. An example is steady heat flow in a conducting medium where temperature T can be measured. The quantity of heat flowing in any direction across unit area is proportional to the space derivative of the temperature in that direction by Newton's law of conduction. When the temperature is steady, the net heat flow out of any closed surface S is zero. Using Newton's law the heat flow across the element dS of the closed surface is proportional to $\frac{\partial T}{\partial n} dS$ and therefore, for the net flow across the closed surface to be zero,

$$\int_{S} \frac{\partial T}{\partial n} dS = 0. \quad (8)$$

But equation (8) is identical to equation (6), i.e. T satisfies Laplace's equation.

In all four applications, gravitation, electrostatics, fluid flow and heat conduction, the mathematical problem will be to solve Laplace's equation subject to the appropriate

7

boundary conditions and then, except in the case of heat conduction, to deduce the appropriate vector field by use of equation (7).

2. LAPLACE'S EQUATION IN ORTHOGONAL CURVILINEAR CO-ORDINATES

The simplest co-ordinate system is the rectangular Cartesian. In solving particular problems it is often easier to use a more complicated co-ordinate system, if this means that one (or more) of the boundaries of the body considered would then coincide with a surface (or surfaces) on which one of the co-ordinates is constant. For example, for problems involving cylinders or spheres, cylindrical polar or spherical polar co-ordinates respectively are generally employed.

There are an infinite number of possible co-ordinate systems. It is only necessary to have three infinite families of surfaces so that one surface of each family passes through each point in space. If a number is attached to each surface in a given family, then the co-ordinates of any point are the numbers attached to the three surfaces passing through the point. e.g., in the rectangular Cartesian system, one family of surfaces are planes whose normals are parallel to a fixed direction, the second family planes whose normals are parallel to a direction orthogonal to the first direction and the third family planes whose normals are parallel to the direction orthogonal to both the first two directions. The number attached to any plane in the Cartesian system is the perpendicular distance from a fixed point, known as the origin, to that plane.

Two surfaces intersect in general in a curve in three-dimensional space. Consider a curve formed by the intersection of two surfaces from different families. Since the curve lies on both surfaces, the two co-ordinates associated with the two surfaces will be constant on the curve and only the third co-ordinate will vary. We shall assume henceforth that this third co-ordinate varies continuously along any curve of intersection of two surfaces from different families, except possibly at singular points of the co-ordinate system (e.g. the origin in polar co-ordinates).

To be more specific, let us call the constant co-ordinates on the curve q_2 and q_3 and the variable co-ordinate q_1. Consider any point (q_1, q_2, q_3) on the curve and another point on the curve, a distance ds_1 away, with co-ordinates (q_1+dq_1, q_2, q_3). Then we define h_1 as the limit of the ratio ds_1/dq_1 as $dq_1 \to +0$. In general h_1 is a function of q_1, q_2, and q_3. In terms of differentials, the relationship is written

$$ds_1 = h_1(q_1, q_2, q_3)\, dq_1.$$

This definition can be illustrated by plane polar co-ordinates in two dimensions. The curves $q_1 = r = $ constant are circles, the curves $q_2 = \theta = $ constant are radii. Consider any point P with co-ordinates (r, θ), $r > 0$ and $0 < \theta < 2\pi$.

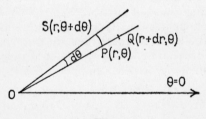

FIG. 4

A point Q at a distance ds_1 from P on the curve

$$q_2 = \theta = \text{constant}$$

through P has co-ordinates $(r+dr, \theta)$. Hence

$$ds_1 = h_1\, dq_1 = h_1\, dr.$$

Since the r co-ordinate measures distance from the origin O, $dr = ds_1$ and therefore $h_1 = 1$. A point S at a distance ds_2 from P on the curve $q_1 = r = $ constant through P has co-ordinates $(r, \theta+d\theta)$. Hence

$$ds_2 = h_2\, dq_2 = h_2\, d\theta.$$

Since PQ is an arc of radius r and subtends angle $\mathrm{d}\theta$ at its centre, $\mathrm{d}s_2 = r\,\mathrm{d}\theta$. Therefore $h_2 = r$.

Returning to the general three-dimensional space, we next consider a curve formed by the intersection of a pair of surfaces, on one of which q_3 is constant and on the other q_1 is constant. This leads to a definition of $h_2(q_1, q_2, q_3)$ as $\lim_{\mathrm{d}q_2 \to 0} \mathrm{d}s_2/\mathrm{d}q_2$ on such a curve. Similarly $h_3(q_1, q_2, q_3)$ is defined as $\lim_{\mathrm{d}q_3 \to 0} \mathrm{d}s_3/\mathrm{d}q_3$ on a curve on which q_1 and q_2 are constant. For convenience we collect the three definitions together in differential form:

$$\left. \begin{aligned} \mathrm{d}s_1 &= h_1\,\mathrm{d}q_1 \\ \mathrm{d}s_2 &= h_2\,\mathrm{d}q_2 \\ \mathrm{d}s_3 &= h_3\,\mathrm{d}q_3, \end{aligned} \right\} \quad (9)$$

where h_1, h_2 and h_3 are functions in general of q_1, q_2 and q_3.

At any point the three curves, given by two of the co-ordinates being constant in turn, define in general three distinct directions in space. If these directions are mutually orthogonal at all points where they are defined,[†] then the co-ordinates are said to form a system of 'orthogonal curvilinear co-ordinates'. Consider any point Q a small distance $\mathrm{d}s$ from $P(q_1, q_2, q_3)$. The vector $\overrightarrow{PQ}$ can be resolved into the sum of three vectors, each parallel to one of the curves through P on which two co-ordinates are constant, and of magnitude $\mathrm{d}s_1$, $\mathrm{d}s_2$ and $\mathrm{d}s_3$. Since these three vectors are mutually orthogonal, by Pythagoras's theorem

$$(\mathrm{d}s)^2 = (\mathrm{d}s_1)^2 + (\mathrm{d}s_2)^2 + (\mathrm{d}s_3)^2.$$

This equation is not true for non-orthogonal co-ordinates. We shall use this equation in section 3. We now proceed to find Laplace's equation in orthogonal curvilinear co-ordinates.

The six surfaces $q_1 = Q_1 \pm \tfrac{1}{2}\mathrm{d}q_1$, $q_2 = Q_2 \pm \tfrac{1}{2}\mathrm{d}q_2$ and

---

† This qualification is required because the directions are not defined at singular points, e.g. what is the direction r increasing at the origin for polar co-ordinates?

$q_3 = Q_3 \pm \frac{1}{2}dq_3$ bound a small curvilinear parallelepiped about the point with co-ordinates (Q_1, Q_2, Q_3). The directions of q_1, q_2 and q_3 increasing are marked in the figure below. We shall now evaluate the surface integral $\int_s \frac{\partial \phi}{\partial n} \, dS$ over this closed surface.

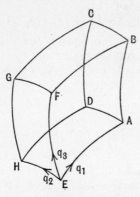

FIG. 5

First consider the contribution from the curvilinear rectangle, the face $ABCD$. q_2 increases from $Q_2 - \frac{1}{2}dq_2$ to $Q_2 + \frac{1}{2}dq_2$, q_3 increases from $Q_3 - \frac{1}{2}dq_3$ to $Q_3 + \frac{1}{2}dq_3$ and q_1 is constant and equal to $Q_1 + \frac{1}{2}dq_1$ on this face. The area of the face is therefore $(h_2 \, dq_2)(h_3 \, dq_3)$ where h_2 and h_3 are evaluated at $Q_1 + \frac{1}{2}dq_1, Q_2, Q_3$. The normal to the face lies in the direction q_1 increasing, the element of length on it is $h_1 \, dq_1$, and the normal derivative $\frac{\partial \phi}{\partial n}$ is $\frac{1}{h_1} \frac{\partial \phi}{\partial q_1}$. The contribution to the surface integral is therefore

$$\left(h_2 h_3 \frac{1}{h_1} \frac{\partial \phi}{\partial q_1} \right)_{Q_1 + \frac{1}{2}dq_1, \, Q_2, \, Q_3} dq_2 \, dq_3,$$

where the expression in brackets is to be evaluated at $Q_1 + \frac{1}{2}dq_1, Q_2, Q_3$, as indicated by the suffices.

Similarly the contribution from the face $EFGH$ is

11

$$-\left(h_2 h_3 \frac{1}{h_1} \frac{\partial \phi}{\partial q_1}\right) Q_1 - \tfrac{1}{2}\mathrm{d}q_1,\ Q_2,\ Q_3, \quad \mathrm{d}q_2\ \mathrm{d}q_3,$$

because the normal now lies in the direction q_1 decreasing. The sum of the contributions from the two faces is, by Taylor's theorem,

$$\left[\frac{\partial}{\partial q_1}\left(\frac{h_2 h_3}{h_1} \frac{\partial \phi}{\partial q_1}\right)\right] Q_1,\ Q_2,\ Q_3 \quad \mathrm{d}q_1,\ \mathrm{d}q_2,\ \mathrm{d}q_3,$$

where the expression in square brackets is evaluated at Q_1, Q_2, Q_3. The contributions from the other two pairs of faces can be written down from symmetry. Adding and substituting in equation (6), we obtain

$$\left[\frac{\partial}{\partial q_1}\left(\frac{h_2 h_3}{h_1} \frac{\partial \phi}{\partial q_1}\right) + \frac{\partial}{\partial q_2}\left(\frac{h_3 h_1}{h_2} \frac{\partial \phi}{\partial q_2}\right)\right.$$
$$\left. + \frac{\partial}{\partial q_3}\left(\frac{h_1 h_2}{h_3} \frac{\partial \phi}{\partial q_3}\right)\right] Q_1,\ Q_2,\ Q_3 \quad \mathrm{d}q_1\ \mathrm{d}q_2\ \mathrm{d}q_3 = 0.$$

$\mathrm{d}q_1$, $\mathrm{d}q_2$ and $\mathrm{d}q_3$ are all non-zero. The argument is valid for a curvilinear parallelepiped about any point so that the suffixes Q_1, Q_2, Q_3 can be dropped. Hence

$$\frac{\partial}{\partial q_1}\left(\frac{h_2 h_3}{h_1} \frac{\partial \phi}{\partial q_1}\right) + \frac{\partial}{\partial q_2}\left(\frac{h_3 h_1}{h_2} \frac{\partial \phi}{\partial q_2}\right) + \frac{\partial}{\partial q_3}\left(\frac{h_1 h_2}{h_3} \frac{\partial \phi}{\partial q_3}\right) = 0. \tag{10}$$

This is Laplace's equation in orthogonal curvilinear co-ordinates.

3. LAPLACE'S EQUATION IN PARTICULAR CO-ORDINATE SYSTEMS

In this section we shall find the forms of equation (10) pertinent to particular co-ordinate systems, i.e. we find h_1, h_2 and h_3 in these systems and then substitute in equation (10). The h are most easily obtained by observing that, since the co-ordinate systems are orthogonal, the general element of length $\mathrm{d}s$ is given by

$$(\mathrm{d}s)^2 = (\mathrm{d}s_1)^2 + (\mathrm{d}s_2)^2 + (\mathrm{d}s_3)^2;$$
$$(\mathrm{d}s)^2 = h_1{}^2(\mathrm{d}q_1)^2 + h_2{}^2(\mathrm{d}q_2)^2 + h_3{}^2(\mathrm{d}q_3)^2. \tag{11}$$

If, therefore, we can write down the square of the element of length, it is only necessary to pick out the coefficients of the $\mathrm{d}q$ to determine the h.

(a) Rectangular Cartesian co-ordinates (x, y, z).

The element of length is

$$(\mathrm{d}s)^2 = (\mathrm{d}x)^2 + (\mathrm{d}y)^2 + (\mathrm{d}z)^2. \tag{12}$$

Therefore, putting $q_1 = x$, $q_2 = y$, $q_3 = z$, $h_1 = h_2 = h_3 = 1$, and equation (10) becomes

$$\frac{\partial^2 \phi}{\partial x^2} + \frac{\partial^2 \phi}{\partial y^2} + \frac{\partial^2 \phi}{\partial z^2} = 0. \tag{13}$$

This is Laplace's equation in rectangular Cartesian co-ordinates.

(b) Cylindrical polar co-ordinates (r, θ, z).

These co-ordinates are related to the Cartesian co-ordinates by

$$x = r \cos \theta, \quad y = r \sin \theta, \quad z = z.$$

Substituting in equation (12),

$$(\mathrm{d}s)^2 = (\mathrm{d}r)^2 + r^2 (\mathrm{d}\theta)^2 + (\mathrm{d}z)^2.$$

Therefore putting $q_1 = r$, $q_2 = \theta$, $q_3 = z$,

$$h_1 = 1, \quad h_2 = r, \quad h_3 = 1.$$

Laplace's equation (10) becomes

$$\frac{\partial}{\partial r}\left(r\frac{\partial \phi}{\partial r}\right) + \frac{\partial}{\partial \theta}\left(\frac{1}{r}\frac{\partial \phi}{\partial \theta}\right) + \frac{\partial}{\partial z}\left(r\frac{\partial \phi}{\partial z}\right) = 0.$$

or
$$\tag{14}$$

$$\frac{\partial^2 \phi}{\partial r^2} + \frac{1}{r}\frac{\partial \phi}{\partial r} + \frac{1}{r^2}\frac{\partial^2 \phi}{\partial \theta^2} + \frac{\partial^2 \phi}{\partial z^2} = 0.$$

(c) Spherical polar co-ordinates (r, θ, ψ).

These co-ordinates are related to the Cartesian co-ordinates by

$$x = r \sin \theta \cos \psi, \quad y = r \sin \theta \sin \psi \text{ and } z = r \cos \theta.$$

Substituting in equation (12),

$$(\mathrm{d}s)^2 = (\mathrm{d}r)^2 + r^2 (\mathrm{d}\theta)^2 + r^2 \sin^2 \theta \, (\mathrm{d}\psi)^2.$$

Therefore, putting $q_1 = r$, $q_2 = \theta$, $q_3 = \psi$,

$$h_1 = 1, \quad h_2 = r, \quad h_3 = r \sin \theta.$$

Laplace's equation (10) becomes

$$\frac{\partial}{\partial r}\left(r^2 \sin\theta \frac{\partial\phi}{\partial r}\right) + \frac{\partial}{\partial\theta}\left(\sin\theta \frac{\partial\phi}{\partial\theta}\right) + \frac{\partial}{\partial\psi}\left(\frac{1}{\sin\theta} \frac{\partial\phi}{\partial\psi}\right) = 0$$

or

$$\frac{\partial^2\phi}{\partial r^2} + \frac{2}{r}\frac{\partial\phi}{\partial r} + \frac{1}{r^2}\frac{\partial^2\phi}{\partial\theta^2} + \frac{\cot\theta}{r^2}\frac{\partial\phi}{\partial\theta} + \frac{1}{r^2\sin^2\theta}\frac{\partial^2\phi}{\partial\psi^2} = 0. \tag{15}$$

Exercises are set throughout this book. The reader is recommended to attempt all of them. Answers are given where required.

Exercise 1

Determine Laplace's equation in parabolic cylinder co-ordinates (ξ, η, z), where $x = \xi\eta$, $y = \frac{1}{2}(\xi^2 - \eta^2)$ and $z = z$.

Exercise 2

Determine Laplace's equation in parabolic co-ordinates (ξ, η, ψ), where $x = \xi\eta\cos\psi$, $y = \xi\eta\sin\psi$ and $z = \frac{1}{2}(\xi^2 - \eta^2)$.

Exercise 3

Determine Laplace's equation in elliptic co-ordinates (ξ, η, ψ), where $x = c\sqrt{(1-\eta^2)(\xi^2-1)}\cos\psi$, $y = c\sqrt{(1-\eta^2)(\xi^2-1)}\sin\psi$ and $z = c\xi\eta$, c constant, $\xi^2 \geqslant 1$, $\eta^2 \leqslant 1$.

Answer 1

$$\frac{\partial^2\phi}{\partial\xi^2} + \frac{\partial^2\phi}{\partial\eta^2} + (\xi^2 + \eta^2)\frac{\partial^2\phi}{\partial z^2} = 0.$$

Answer 2

$$\frac{1}{\xi}\frac{\partial}{\partial\xi}\left(\xi\frac{\partial\phi}{\partial\xi}\right) + \frac{1}{\eta}\frac{\partial}{\partial\eta}\left(\eta\frac{\partial\phi}{\partial\eta}\right) + \left(\frac{1}{\xi^2} + \frac{1}{\eta^2}\right)\frac{\partial^2\phi}{\partial\psi^2} = 0.$$

Answer 3

$$\frac{\partial}{\partial\xi}\left[(\xi^2-1)\frac{\partial\phi}{\partial\xi}\right] + \frac{\partial}{\partial\eta}\left[(1-\eta^2)\frac{\partial\phi}{\partial\eta}\right] + \frac{\xi^2-\eta^2}{(1-\eta^2)(\xi^2-1)}\frac{\partial^2\phi}{\partial\psi^2} = 0.$$

CHAPTER TWO

The Method of Separation of Variables

1. RECTANGULAR CARTESIAN CO-ORDINATES

Consider a partial differential equation for ϕ in any number of independent variables, x, y, z, ... t. The method of separation of variables is used to find solutions of the form

$$\phi = X(x)\ Y(y)\ Z(z) \ldots T(t), \qquad (16)$$

where $X(x)$ is a function of x only, $Y(y)$ a function of y only, ... and $T(t)$ a function of t only.

One substitutes from equation (16) into the differential equation and attempts to manipulate the resulting equation into the sum of two parts such that the two parts have no independent variable in common. Then the two parts are separately constant. Generally what happens is that one part is a function of one variable only and the other part contains all the other variables. We shall now prove the constancy of each part in this case. Suppose, for the purpose of the argument, that one part contains the variable x only, and that x does not appear in the second part. Then the first part is either a function of x or a constant. If it were a function of x, then for the equation to be satisfied for all x the second part of the equation would have to depend on x. But this is contrary to the hypothesis that the second part does not contain x. Hence both parts are equal to constants, which are equal in magnitude and opposite in sign to satisfy the equation. If the original equation contained more than two variables, then, after one part has been 'separated out' as an equation in one variable, the other part will contain two or more variables. One now attempts to repeat the process until all the variables have been separated. If this is successful, instead of the original partial differential equation in n variables, one will have n ordinary differential equations containing $n-1$ arbitrary constants. Each equation will need to be solved for one of $X(x)$, $Y(y)$, $Z(z)$, ... $T(t)$ and the result substituted back into equation (16). If the partial differential equation is linear and homogeneous, then the sum of any number of solutions is itself a solution.† In particular solutions of the form of equation (16) can be added to provide solutions of more complicated form; hence the method of separation of variables can lead to the solution of a wide group of problems.

We shall now apply the method to Laplace's equation in rectangular Cartesian co-ordinates, equation (13),

$$\frac{\partial^2 \phi}{\partial x^2} + \frac{\partial^2 \phi}{\partial y^2} + \frac{\partial^2 \phi}{\partial z^2} = 0. \tag{13}$$

Substitute

$$\phi = X(x)\, Y(y)\, Z(z). \tag{17}$$

This gives

$$X''(x)Y(y)Z(z) + X(x)Y''(y)Z(z) + X(x)Y(y)Z''(z) = 0, \tag{18}$$

where a dash denotes a derivative of a function with respect to its argument. Note that this notation is only applicable to functions of one variable. Divide through equation (18) by $X(x)\, Y(y)\, Z(z)$:

$$\frac{X''(x)}{X(x)} + \frac{Y''(y)}{Y(y)} + \frac{Z''(z)}{Z(z)} = 0. \tag{19}$$

Hurrah! We have succeeded, not only in separating one variable, but in separating all the variables at one go. The first term is a function of x only, the second of y only and the third of z only. They must all be constant. If a and b are arbitrary constants, real or complex, put the first term

---

† This proved by direct substitution. If $\phi_1, \phi_2 \ldots \phi_n$ are solutions, then substitution of $\phi = \phi_1 + \phi_2 + \ldots + \phi_n$ shows that ϕ is also a solution.

equal to a and the second to b; to satisfy equation (19), the third term must equal $-a-b$.

i.e.

$$\frac{d^2X}{dx^2} - aX = 0, \tag{20}$$

$$\frac{d^2Y}{dy^2} - bY = 0 \tag{21}$$

and

$$\frac{d^2Z}{dz^2} + (a+b)Z = 0. \tag{22}$$

Instead of one partial differential equation, we have three ordinary differential equations to solve. In this case the solutions of all three equations are well known. They can be summarized,

$$X = e^{\pm\sqrt{a}x}, \quad Y = e^{\pm\sqrt{b}y}, \quad Z = e^{\pm i\sqrt{a+b}z}, \quad i = \sqrt{-1}; \tag{23}$$

the solution in each case is the sum of the two possible terms, each one multiplied by an arbitrary constant. Substituting back into equation (17), solutions of equation (13) are given by

$$\phi = C\, e^{\pm\sqrt{a}x}\, e^{\pm\sqrt{b}y}\, e^{\pm i\sqrt{a+b}z} \tag{24}$$

where C is constant; there is a different constant for each of the eight possible combinations of signs. Since equation (13) is linear, a sum of solutions is also a solution. Therefore

$$\phi = \sum_{a,b} C_{ab}\, e^{\pm\sqrt{a}x}\, e^{\pm\sqrt{b}y}\, e^{\pm i\sqrt{a+b}z} \tag{25}$$

is a solution of Laplace's equation. The C_{ab} are sets of eight constants; the sum is over all pairs of constant values of a and b, real or complex, and over the eight possible combinations of sign for each pair a, b.

In two-dimensional problems, there is dependence on x and y only. Solutions of Laplace's equation in two dimensions can be obtained from equation (25) by putting $a+b=0$ because this eliminates the dependence on z. If

$a+b=0$ and both are real, either $a>0$ and $b<0$, or $a<0$ and $b>0$. If $a=b=0$, ϕ reduces to a constant. Suppose $a>0$, put $a=m^2$, then $b=-m^2$ and equation (24) gives

$$\phi=C\,e^{\pm mx}\,e^{\pm imy}. \qquad (26)$$

The different possible forms of equation (26) can be combined to give a solution of the form

$$\phi=A_m \cosh mx \cos my+B_m \cosh mx \sin my$$
$$+C_m \sinh mx \cos my+D_m \sinh mx \sin my, \qquad (27)$$

where A_m, B_m, C_m and D_m are real constants. Equation (27) can be summed over any number of values of m to give further solutions. If $a<0$, putting $b=m^2$ gives solutions analogous to equation (22) with x and y interchanged, i.e.

$$\phi=A_m \cosh my \cos mx+B_m \cosh my \sin mx$$
$$+C_m \sinh my \cos mx+D_m \sinh my \sin mx. \qquad (28)$$

2. TEMPERATURE DISTRIBUTION IN A RECTANGULAR METAL BLOCK

The block has length l, thickness $2h$ and breadth b. Take the origin at the mid-point of AD and the axes as shown in the diagram. The faces $BCGF$ and $ADHE$ are kept at zero temperature and the faces $ABCD$ and $EFGH$ are thermally insulated (i.e. no heat flow across them). Steady tempera-

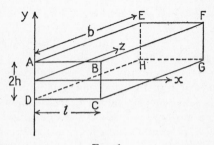

Fig. 6

tures, dependent on the co-ordinate x only, are imposed on each of the faces $ABFE$ and $DCGH$. The problem is to determine the temperature distribution T within the block.

We showed at the end of section 1, chapter 1, that the temperature in a conducting medium satisfied Laplace's equation. The mathematical problem is therefore to find that solution of Laplace's equation which takes the given values of the temperature on the boundaries.

Since the imposed temperature distribution in this case is independent of z, and there is no heat flow across the boundaries whose normals are in the z-direction, we look for a solution which is independent of z; i.e. we treat the problem as effectively two-dimensional. We shall consider just the rectangle $ABCD$ because the temperature at any point in the interior of the block is the same as at that point which is the orthogonal projection of the first point on $ABCD$.

Example 1. Both AB and DC are maintained at temperatures $T_0 \sin \dfrac{\pi x}{l}$. The problem is to solve Laplace's equation subject to the boundary conditions

$$T=0 \text{ when } x=0 \text{ or } x=l \text{ and } T=T_0 \sin \frac{\pi x}{l} \text{ when } y=\pm h.$$
(29)

Since $\sin \dfrac{\pi x}{l}=0$ on $x=0$ and $x=l$, the boundary conditions on $x=0$ and $x=l$ will be satisfied by any solution of the form $T=f(y) \sin\dfrac{\pi x}{l}$ where $f(y)$ is a function of y only. The boundary conditions on $y=\pm h$ will be satisfied if

$$f(y)=T_0 \text{ at } y=\pm h.$$
(30)

Can we find a solution of Laplace's equation of the form $f(y) \sin \dfrac{\pi x}{l}$? Examination of equation (28) shows that, if we put $m=\dfrac{\pi}{l}$, the second and fourth terms of this equation are of the required form; i.e. Laplace's equation is satisfied by

$$T=\left(B \cosh \frac{\pi y}{l}+D \sinh \frac{\pi y}{l}\right) \sin \frac{\pi x}{l}.$$

To satisfy equation (30), $B=T_0 \operatorname{sech} \dfrac{\pi h}{l}$ and $D=0$.

Hence

$$T=T_0 \operatorname{sech} \frac{\pi h}{l} \cosh \frac{\pi y}{l} \sin \frac{\pi x}{l}. \tag{31}$$

Equation (31) is the solution to the problem because it satisfies the governing differential equation and the boundary conditions.

It can be shown that the solution of Laplace's equation within a closed surface S is unique if either the variable ϕ or its normal derivative $\dfrac{\partial \phi}{\partial n}$ is given at all points on S† (see, e.g., O.D. Kellogg, *Potential Theory*, p. 213). Consequently if we can find a particular solution to Laplace's equation that satisfies the boundary conditions on S, which boundary conditions are either ϕ or $\dfrac{\partial \phi}{\partial n}$ given at all points on S, then we know that this is *the* solution irrespective of how it was obtained. Any other solution will give the same values of ϕ at all points within and on S. The form of the two solutions may be different but they will be transformable the one into the other by algebraic manipulation only.

Example 2. The temperature on AB is maintained at $4T_0x(l-x)/l^2$, i.e. parabolic with temperature T_0 at the

---

† There is one exception to this statement. If $\dfrac{\partial \phi}{\partial n}$ is given at all points on S, then the solution is indeterminate to the extent of an arbitrary additive constant. (It only requires ϕ to be given at one point on S for the constant to be found).

midpoint $x = l/2$, and the temperature on CD is zero.

The problem is to solve Laplace's equation subject to the following boundary conditions:

$T = 0$ when $x = 0$ or $x = l$ or $y = -h$, and $T = 4T_0x(l-x)/l^2$ when $y = +h$. (32)

In Example 1 we looked for a solution whose variation with x was identical to that of the non-zero boundary conditions. In this case such a procedure would fail because the non-zero boundary conditions vary quadratically with x and the solutions of Laplace's equation obtained so far, equations (27) and (28), vary either exponentially or sinusoidally with x. We must first convert the boundary conditions to either exponential or sinusoidal form. The latter is possible by Fourier analysis. The temperature on $y = +h$ will be expressed in the form $T = \sum_{n=1}^{\infty} A_n \sin \dfrac{n\pi x}{l}$, n integral.

This reduces the problem to solving Laplace's equation subject to the boundary conditions,

$\phi = 0$ when $x = 0$ or $x = l$ or $y = -h$ and $\phi = A_n \sin \dfrac{n\pi x}{l}$ when $y = +h$, (33)

and then summing the solutions corresponding to the different values of n. The Fourier sine series was chosen, in preference to either the full range or cosine series, because $\sin \dfrac{n\pi x}{l} = 0$ at $x = 0$ and $x = l$ and so the values of temperature remain continuous around the boundary for each value of n.

The coefficients A_n are determined by Fourier's theorem† as

$$A_n = \frac{2}{l} \int_0^l 4T_0x(l-x)/l^2 \sin \frac{n\pi x}{l} \, \mathrm{d}x.$$

† See I. N. Sneddon, *Fourier Series*, uniform with this volume.

This integral is evaluated by twice integrating by parts,

$$A_n = \frac{8T_0}{l^3}\left(-\frac{l}{n\pi}\right)\left[(lx-x^2)\cos\frac{n\pi x}{l}\bigg|_0^l - \int_0^l(l-2x)\cos\frac{n\pi x}{l}dx\right]$$

$$= \frac{8T_0}{l^3}\left(\frac{l}{n\pi}\right)^2\left[(l-2x)\sin\frac{n\pi x}{l}\bigg|_0^l + 2\int_0^l\sin\frac{n\pi x}{l}\,dx\right]$$

$$= -\frac{16T_0}{l^3}\left(\frac{l}{n\pi}\right)^3\cos\frac{n\pi x}{l}\bigg|_0^l = \frac{16T_0}{n^3\pi^3}(1-(-)^n)$$

$$= \frac{32T_0}{n^3\pi^3} \text{ if } n \text{ odd, } =0 \text{ if } n \text{ even.} \tag{34}$$

Solutions of Laplace's equation containing $\sin\dfrac{n\pi x}{l}$ are given by equation (28) with $m=\dfrac{n\pi}{l}$ as

$$\phi = \left(B_n\cosh\frac{n\pi y}{l} + D_n\sinh\frac{n\pi y}{l}\right)\sin\frac{n\pi x}{l}. \tag{35}$$

To satisfy the boundary conditions, equations (33),

$$B_n\cosh\frac{n\pi h}{l} - D_n\sinh\frac{n\pi h}{l} = 0$$

and

$$B_n\cosh\frac{n\pi h}{l} + D_n\sinh\frac{n\pi h}{l} = A_n;$$

whence

$$B_n = \tfrac{1}{2}A_n\operatorname{sech}\frac{n\pi h}{l} \text{ and } D_n = \tfrac{1}{2}A_n\operatorname{cosech}\frac{n\pi h}{l}. \tag{36}$$

Substituting back into equation (35) and using equation (34),

$$\phi = \frac{16T_0}{n^3\pi^3}\left(\operatorname{sech}\frac{n\pi h}{l}\cosh\frac{n\pi y}{l} + \operatorname{cosech}\frac{n\pi h}{l}\sinh\frac{n\pi y}{l}\right)\sin\frac{n\pi x}{l}$$

if n odd,

$\phi = 0$ if n even. \hfill (37)

The final solution for the temperature T is obtained by summing equations (37) over all integral values of n, i.e.

$$T = \frac{16T_0}{\pi^3} \sum_{\substack{n=1 \\ n \text{ odd}}}^{\infty} \frac{1}{n^3} \left(\operatorname{sech} \frac{n\pi h}{l} \cosh \frac{n\pi y}{l} \right.$$

$$\left. + \operatorname{cosech} \frac{n\pi h}{l} \sinh \frac{n\pi y}{l} \right) \sin \frac{n\pi x}{l}, \tag{38}$$

where the sum is over odd values of n only.

Exercise 4

The physical situation is the same as in the examples just solved except that the faces $BCGF$ and $ADHE$ are now thermally insulated instead of being maintained at zero temperature. Find the temperature in the block when, case (i), the temperature distributions on both AB and CD are given by $T = T_0 \cos \frac{\pi x}{l}$ and when, case (ii), the temperature imposed on AB is $T = T_0(3lx^2 - 2x^3)/l^3$ and that on CD is zero.

Hint: Since $\frac{\partial T}{\partial x} = 0$ at $x = 0$ and $x = l$, try Fourier cosine series.

Answers

(i) $T_0 \operatorname{sech} \frac{\pi h}{l} \cosh \frac{\pi y}{l} \cos \frac{\pi x}{l}$,

(ii) $\frac{T_0}{4} \left(1 + \frac{y}{h} \right) - \frac{24T_0}{\pi^4} \sum_{\substack{n=2 \\ n \text{ even}}}^{\infty} \left(\operatorname{cosech} \frac{n\pi h}{l} \sinh \frac{n\pi y}{l} + \operatorname{sech} \frac{n\pi h}{l} \cosh \frac{n\pi y}{l} \right)$

$\cos \frac{n\pi x}{l}$.

3. THE ANALOGOUS ELECTROSTATIC PROBLEM

The problem in electrostatics, analogous to the problem of the previous section, is that of a rectangular parallelepiped of free space surrounded by (i) faces $ABCD$ and $EFGH$ which are insulators, (ii) faces $BCGF$ and $ADHE$ which are conductors and earthed (i.e. $V = 0$), and (iii) faces $ABFE$ and $DCGH$ on each of which the potential V is a given function of x. The problem is to determine the potential and the electric field within the block. Since V satisfies Laplace's equation in free space whenever there are no charges within the volume considered and the boundary conditions on V are the same as those on T in the previous

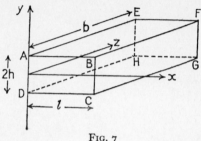

Fig. 7

section, the solution for V is the same as that for T. Hence, using equations (31) and (38):

case i. If $V = V_0 \sin \dfrac{\pi x}{l}$ when $y = \pm h$, then $V = V_0 \operatorname{sech} \dfrac{\pi h}{l}$ $\cosh \dfrac{\pi y}{l} \sin \dfrac{\pi x}{l}$; and

case ii. If $V = 4V\, x(l-x)/l^2$ when $y = +h$ and $V = 0$ when $y = -h$, then

$$V = \frac{16 V_0}{\pi^3} \sum_{\substack{n=1 \\ n\ \mathrm{odd}}}^{\infty} \frac{1}{n^3}\left(\operatorname{sech}\frac{n\pi h}{l}\cosh\frac{n\pi y}{l} + \operatorname{cosech}\frac{n\pi h}{l}\sinh\frac{n\pi y}{l}\right)$$
$$\sin\frac{n\pi x}{l}. \tag{39}$$

The electric field intensity E has components given by partially differentiating V with respect to each space co-ordinate in turn. The components of intensity, when V is given by equation (39), are

$$E_x = -\frac{\partial V}{\partial x} = -\frac{16 V_0}{\pi^2 l} \sum_{\substack{n=1 \\ n\ \mathrm{odd}}}^{\infty} \frac{1}{n^2}\left(\operatorname{sech}\frac{n\pi h}{l}\cosh\frac{n\pi y}{l}\right.$$
$$\left. + \operatorname{cosech}\frac{n\pi h}{l}\sinh\frac{n\pi y}{l}\right)\cos\frac{n\pi x}{l},$$

24

$$E_y = -\frac{\partial V}{\partial y} = -\frac{16 V_0}{\pi^2 l} \sum_{\substack{n=1 \\ n \text{ odd}}}^{\infty} \frac{1}{n^2} \left(\operatorname{sech} \frac{n\pi h}{l} \sinh \frac{n\pi y}{l} \right.$$

$$\left. + \operatorname{cosech} \frac{n\pi h}{l} \cosh \frac{n\pi y}{l} \right) \sin \frac{n\pi x}{l}$$

and

$$E_z = -\frac{\partial V}{\partial z} = 0.$$

4. CYLINDRICAL POLAR CO-ORDINATES

Laplace's equation in cylindrical polar co-ordinates is

$$\frac{\partial^2 \phi}{\partial r^2} + \frac{1}{r} \frac{\partial \phi}{\partial r} + \frac{1}{r^2} \frac{\partial^2 \phi}{\partial \theta^2} + \frac{\partial^2 \phi}{\partial z^2} = 0. \tag{14}$$

We look for a solution of the form

$$\phi = R(r) \, \Theta(\theta) \, Z(z). \tag{40}$$

Substituting from (40) into (14),

$$R''(r)\Theta(\theta)Z(z) + \frac{1}{r}R'(r)\Theta(\theta)Z(z) + \frac{1}{r^2}R(r)\Theta''(\theta)Z(z)$$

$$+ R(r)\Theta(\theta)Z''(z) = 0.$$

Divide through by $R(r)\Theta(\theta)Z(z)$,

$$\frac{R''(r)}{R(r)} + \frac{R'(r)}{rR(r)} + \frac{1}{r^2}\frac{\Theta''(\theta)}{\Theta(\theta)} + \frac{Z''(z)}{Z(z)} = 0.$$

The last term is a function of z only. The remaining three terms do not contain z. Therefore the last term is a constant, say 'a'.

i.e.

$$\frac{\mathrm{d}^2 Z}{\mathrm{d}z^2} - aZ = 0 \tag{41}$$

and

$$\frac{R''}{R} + \frac{R'}{rR} + \frac{1}{r^2}\frac{\Theta''}{\Theta} + a = 0.$$

Multiply the last equation through by r^2,

$$r^2 \frac{R''}{R} + \frac{rR'}{R} + ar^2 + \frac{\Theta''}{\Theta} = 0.$$

The terms are now separable. Θ''/Θ is a constant, called for convenience $-n^2$.

i.e.

$$\frac{\mathrm{d}^2\Theta}{\mathrm{d}\theta^2} + n^2\Theta = 0 \tag{42}$$

and

$$\frac{\mathrm{d}^2 R}{\mathrm{d}r^2} + \frac{1}{r}\frac{\mathrm{d}R}{\mathrm{d}r} + \left(a - \frac{n^2}{r^2}\right)R = 0. \tag{43}$$

Equations (41) and (42) have solutions

$$Z = A_1 \, e^{\sqrt{a}\,z} + A_2 \, e^{-\sqrt{a}\,z} \tag{44}$$

and

$$\Theta = B_1 \cos n\theta + B_2 \sin n\theta, \tag{45}$$

where A_1, A_2, B_1 and B_2 are constants. However the solutions of equation (43), except for $a=0$, cannot be expressed in terms of a finite number of rational functions and/or trigonometric and exponential functions. Equation (43) is one form of what is known as *Bessel's equation*, and we shall investigate its solutions in the next chapter. These solutions with equations (44) and (45) will enable us to substitute back for R, Θ and Z into equation (40) and so to obtain solutions of Laplace's equations in cylindrical polar co-ordinates. We shall then be able to construct solutions to some particular problems in the same manner as solutions were constructed using rectangular Cartesian co-ordinates in sections 2 and 3. In the meantime note that if the problem is such that the co-ordinate θ covers its entire range from 0 to 2π for any fixed values of r and z, then, for the function Θ to be single-valued, Θ must have the same value at $\theta=0$ and $\theta=2\pi$. From equation (45) this requires n to be integral. Without loss of generality n can be taken as a positive integer or zero. This condition is generally, but not always, satisfied in practical problems.

5. SPHERICAL POLAR CO-ORDINATES

Laplace's equation in spherical polar co-ordinates is

$$\frac{\partial}{\partial r}\left(r^2\frac{\partial \phi}{\partial r}\right)+\frac{1}{\sin \theta}\ \frac{\partial}{\partial \theta}\left(\sin \theta\ \frac{\partial \phi}{\partial \theta}\right)+\frac{1}{\sin^2\theta}\ \frac{\partial^2 \phi}{\partial \psi^2}=0. \quad (15)$$

We look for a solution of the form

$$\phi=R(r)\ \Theta(\theta)\ \Psi(\psi). \quad (46)$$

Substitute from equation (46) into equation (15) and divide through by $R(r)\ \Theta(\theta)\ \Psi(\psi)$:

$$\frac{1}{R}\frac{d}{dr}\left(r^2\frac{dR}{dr}\right)+\frac{1}{\Theta\sin\theta}\frac{d}{d\theta}\left(\sin\theta\frac{d\Theta}{d\theta}\right)+\frac{1}{\Psi\sin^2\theta}\frac{d^2\Psi}{d\psi^2}=0. \quad (47)$$

In equation (47) the first term is dependent on r, the other two independent of r. It is convenient to choose the arbitrary constant as $n(n+1)$ so that

$$\frac{1}{R}\ \frac{d}{dr}\left(r^2\frac{dR}{dr}\right)=n(n+1) \quad (48)$$

and

$$n(n+1)\sin^2\theta+\frac{\sin \theta}{\Theta}\ \frac{d}{d\theta}\left(\sin \theta\ \frac{d\Theta}{d\theta}\right)+\frac{1}{\Psi}\ \frac{d^2\Psi}{d\psi^2}=0.$$

This equation is now separable. If the arbitrary constant is m^2,

$$(n(n+1)\sin^2\theta-m^2)\ \Theta+\sin \theta\ \frac{d}{d\theta}\left(\sin \theta\ \frac{d\Theta}{d\theta}\right)=0 \quad (49)$$

and

$$\frac{d^2\Psi}{d\psi^2}+m^2\Psi=0. \quad (50)$$

Equation (48) has solution

$$R=C_n r^n+D_n r^{-n-1}, \quad (51)$$

where C_n and D_n are constants. Equation (50) has solution

$$\Psi=A_m \cos m\psi+B_m \sin m\psi \quad (52)$$

where A_m and B_m are constants. If in a particular problem ψ covers the entire range from 0 to 2π, then for Ψ to be single valued m must be integral. Without loss of generality, m can be taken to be a positive integer or zero. m will be assumed to take one of these values henceforth in this book.

27

Equation (49) can be reduced to the *associated Legendre equation*. Its solution is the subject of Chapter 5. When solutions have been obtained, substitution for Θ and for R and Ψ from equations (51) and (52) into equation (46) gives solutions of Laplace's equation from which solutions of particular problems can be constructed.

Exercise 5

If ϕ satisfies a partial differential equation in x, y, z and t and if a substitution of the form $\phi = \psi(x, y)\chi(z, t)$, where ψ is a function of x and y only and χ of z and t only, enables the equation to be separated into two parts such that the first part contains only the variables x and y and the latter only z and t, show that the two parts are separately constant.

CHAPTER THREE

Bessel Functions

---

1. AN INFINITE SERIES SOLUTION OF BESSEL'S EQUATION

In chapter 2, section 4, we derived the equation

$$\frac{d^2R}{dr^2}+\frac{1}{r}\frac{dR}{dr}+\left(a-\frac{n^2}{r^2}\right)R=0. \tag{43}$$

The treatment of this equation depends on whether $a=0$, $a>0$ or $a<0$. If $a=0$ and $n>0$, equation (43) becomes a homogeneous equation with solution $R=Ar^n+Br^{-n}$. We shall consider the case $a>0$ in this section, and treat $a<0$ in section 4. The constant n is positive or zero, not necessarily an integer.

When $a>0$, put $a=\alpha^2$ where $\alpha>0$. By a change of independent variable, α can be eliminated from equation (43). We introduce a new independent variable ρ defined by

$$\rho=\alpha r=\sqrt{a}\,r \tag{53}$$

and consider R as a function of ρ. Since $\dfrac{d\rho}{dr}=\alpha$,

$$\frac{1}{r}\frac{dR}{dr}=\frac{\alpha}{\rho}\frac{dR}{d\rho}\frac{d\rho}{dr}=\frac{\alpha^2}{\rho}\frac{dR}{d\rho},$$

$$\frac{d^2R}{dr^2}=\frac{d}{dr}\left(\frac{dR}{dr}\right)=\frac{d\rho}{dr}\frac{d}{d\rho}\left(\frac{d\rho}{dr}\frac{dR}{d\rho}\right)=\alpha^2\frac{d^2R}{d\rho^2}$$

and

$$\frac{n^2}{r^2}=\frac{\alpha^2n^2}{\rho^2}.$$

Substituting in equation (43) and dividing through by α^2,

$$\frac{d^2R}{d\rho^2}+\frac{1}{\rho}\frac{dR}{d\rho}+\left(1-\frac{n^2}{\rho^2}\right)R=0. \tag{54}$$

This equation is known as Bessel's equation for functions of order n.

Since the solutions of this equation are not elementary functions, let us see if we can solve the equation by an infinite series of the form

$$R(\rho) = \rho^\gamma \left(a_0 + a_1\rho + \frac{a_2}{2!}\rho^2 + \frac{a_3}{3!}\rho^3 + \cdots \right) = \rho^\gamma \sum_{r=0}^{\infty} a_r \frac{\rho^r}{r!}, \quad (55)$$

where we are free to choose the constants γ, a_0, a_1, a_2, etc., to satisfy the differential equation and $a_0 \neq 0$. Differentiating equation (55) twice in succession,

$$\frac{dR}{d\rho} = a_0\gamma\rho^{\gamma-1} + a_1(\gamma+1)\rho^\gamma + \frac{a_2}{2!}(\gamma+2)\rho^{\gamma+1} + \frac{a_3}{3!}(\gamma+3)\rho^{\gamma+2}$$
$$+ \cdots \qquad (56)$$

and

$$\frac{d^2R}{d\rho^2} = a_0\gamma(\gamma-1)\rho^{\gamma-2} + a_1(\gamma+1)\gamma\rho^{\gamma-1} + \frac{a_2}{2!}(\gamma+2)(\gamma+1)\rho^\gamma$$
$$+ \cdots \qquad (57)$$

We now substitute from equations (55), (56) and (57) into equation (54). This gives an infinite series in powers of ρ whose sum is equal to zero. But the sum must be equal to zero for all values of ρ and this can only be the case if the coefficient of each power of ρ is zero. The powers of ρ are in succession $\gamma-2$, $\gamma-1$, γ, $\gamma+1$, etc. Let us start by equating the coefficient of the lowest power of ρ to zero,† then the next three lowest and finally the general power $\rho^{\gamma+r}$. We shall place in square brackets on the left of the equation the power whose coefficient is equated to zero.

$[\rho^{\gamma-2}]$ $\qquad a_0\gamma(\gamma-1) + a_0\gamma - a_0n^2 = 0,$ $\qquad (58)$

$[\rho^{\gamma-1}]$ $\qquad a_1(\gamma+1)\gamma + a_1(\gamma+1) - a_1n^2 = 0,$ $\qquad (59)$

$[\rho^\gamma]$ $\qquad \frac{a_2}{2!}(\gamma+2)(\gamma+1) + \frac{a_2}{2!}(\gamma+2) + a_0 - \frac{a_2}{2!}n^2 = 0,$ $\qquad (60)$

† The equation obtained by equating the coefficient of the owest power to zero is known in the theory of differential equations as the 'indicial equation'.

$[\rho^{\gamma+1}]$ $\dfrac{a_3}{3!}(\gamma+3)(\gamma+2)+\dfrac{a_3}{3!}(\gamma+3)+a_1-\dfrac{a_3}{3!}n^2=0,$ (61)

$[\rho^{\gamma+r}]$ $\dfrac{a_{r+2}}{(r+2)!}(\gamma+r+2)(\gamma+r+1)+\dfrac{a_{r+2}}{(r+2)!}(\gamma+r+2)$

$$+\dfrac{a_r}{r!}-\dfrac{a_{r+2}}{(r+2)!}n^2=0.$$ (62)

Since $a_0 \neq 0$, equation (58) is satisfied if

$$\gamma = \pm n.$$ (63)

Equation (59), which can be written $a_1\{(\gamma+1)^2-n^2\}=0$, is only consistent with equation (63) if $a_1=0$. From equation (60) on putting $n^2=\gamma^2$,

$$\dfrac{a_2}{2!}((\gamma+2)^2-\gamma^2)+a_0=0$$

or

$$a_2 = -\dfrac{a_0}{2(\gamma+1)}.$$ (64)

Equation (61) gives $a_3=0$ since $a_1=0$. From equation (62), on putting $n^2=\gamma^2$,

$$\dfrac{a_{r+2}}{(r+2)!}((\gamma+r-2)^2-\gamma^2)+\dfrac{a_r}{r!}=0$$

or

$$a_{r+2} = -\dfrac{r+1}{2\gamma+r+2}a_r.$$ (65)

Since $a_1=a_3=0$, equation (65) gives in succession $a_5=0$, $a_7=0$, etc., i.e.

$$a_r=0 \text{ for } r \text{ odd.}$$ (66)

The relation between a_r and a_{r-2} is obtained by replacing r in equation (65) by $r-2$. This gives

$$a_r = -\dfrac{r-1}{2\gamma+r}a_{r-2}$$ (65a)

For r even, put $r=2s$ in equation (65a). Then

31

$$a_{2s} = -\frac{2s-1}{2(\gamma+s)}a_{2s-2}$$

$$= (-)^2 \frac{(2s-1)(2s-3)}{2^2(\gamma+s)(\gamma+s-1)} a_{2s-4}$$

$$= (-)^s \frac{(2s-1)(2s-3)(2s-5)\ldots 3.1}{2^s(\gamma+s)(\gamma+s-1)(\gamma+s-2)\ldots(\gamma+1)} a_0.$$

Now $(2s-1)(2s-3)(2s-5)\ldots 3.1$

$$= \frac{2s(2s-1)(2s-2)\ldots 1}{2s(2s-2)(2s-4)\ldots 2}$$

$$= \frac{(2s)!}{2^s.s(s-1)(s-2)\ldots 1}$$

$$= \frac{(2s)!}{2^s.s!}$$

and $(\gamma+s)(\gamma+s-1)\ldots(\gamma+1) = (\gamma+s)!/\gamma!$.
Therefore

$$a_r = a_{2s} = (-)^s \frac{(2s)!\,\gamma!}{2^{2s}.s!\,(\gamma+s)!} a_0, \quad r \text{ even.} \qquad (67)$$

In writing down the last two equations, the factorial function $\gamma!$ has been implicitly extended to non-integral values of γ. The definition of $\gamma!$ for non-integral values of γ should be such that the characteristic property for integral γ, namely $(\gamma+1)! = (\gamma+1)(\gamma!)$, is satisfied for all γ and such that the definition reduces to the usual definition for integral γ. It will now be shown that the definition

$$\gamma! = \int_0^\infty e^{-t} t^\gamma \, dt \quad \text{for } \gamma \geqslant 0$$

has the required properties. The integral converges at both limits.

Now

$$(\gamma+1)! = \int_0^\infty e^{-t} t^{\gamma+1} \, dt;$$

integrating by parts,

$$(\gamma+1)! = -e^{-t} t^{\gamma+1} \Big|_0^\infty + \int_0^\infty e^{-t} (\gamma+1) t^\gamma \, dt$$

$$= (\gamma+1)(\gamma!).$$

Also

$$0! = \int_0^\infty e^{-t} \, dt = 1,$$

and when γ is a positive integer, using the characteristic property just proved,

$$\gamma! = \gamma((\gamma-1)!) = \gamma(\gamma-1)((\gamma-2)!) = \gamma(\gamma-1)(\gamma-2) \ldots 1 . 0!$$
$$= \gamma(\gamma-1)(\gamma-2) \ldots 1,$$

which is the usual definition of $\gamma!$. $\gamma!$ is denoted in many books by the gamma function $\Gamma(\gamma+1)$. Note that the gamma function has argument greater by unity than the equivalent factorial function. For γ negative, we shall invert the characteristic property $(\gamma+1)! = (\gamma+1)(\gamma!)$ to define $\gamma!$ by

$$\gamma! = \frac{(\gamma+1)!}{\gamma+1} = \frac{(\gamma+2)!}{(\gamma+1)(\gamma+2)}$$
$$= \frac{(\gamma+r)!}{(\gamma+1)(\gamma+2) \ldots (\gamma+r)},$$

where r is chosen so that $0 \leqslant \gamma+r < 1$. Note that $\gamma!$ is infinite for finite γ if and only if γ is a negative integer.

Substitute back for the a_r from equation (66) and (67) into equation (55). Hence, using equation (63), we have two solutions of equation (54) given by

$$R_1(\rho) = a_0 n! \sum_{s=0}^\infty (-)^s \frac{1}{s!(n+s)!} \left(\frac{\rho}{2}\right)^{n+2s}$$

and

$$R_2(\rho) = a_0(-n)! \sum_{s=0}^\infty (-)^s \frac{1}{s!(-n+s)!} \left(\frac{\rho}{2}\right)^{-n+2s}.$$

If we introduce $J_\gamma(\rho)$ to denote

$$J_\gamma(\rho) = \sum_{s=0}^\infty \frac{(-)^s}{s!(\gamma+s)!} \left(\frac{\rho}{2}\right)^{\gamma+2s}, \tag{68}$$

then, apart from arbitrary multiplicative constants, the two solutions of Bessel's equation, equation (54), are given by $J_n(\rho)$ and $J_{-n}(\rho)$. $J_\gamma(\rho)$ is called either a Bessel coefficient or a Bessel function of the first kind. It is said to be of order γ.

We must verify that the infinite series, by which the Bessel function is defined, is convergent. The ratio of the absolute values of two successive terms in the series is $\left|\left(\dfrac{\rho}{2}\right)^2 \big/ s(\gamma+s)\right|$ which tends to zero as $s \to \infty$ for all ρ, real or complex. Therefore, by the ratio test,† the series is absolutely convergent for all ρ, real or complex.

A second order differential equation has two linearly independent solutions and any other solution is expressible as a linear combination of these two. To see whether any solution of Bessel's equation of order n is expressible as a linear combination of J_n and J_{-n}, we must find out whether or not J_n and J_{-n} are linearly independent.

In the neighbourhood of the origin, i.e. near $\rho=0$, the value of $J_\gamma(\rho)$ will be very nearly equal to the first non-zero term in the series. If the coefficient of the first term in the series on the right-hand side of equation (68) is non-zero, i.e. $\dfrac{1}{\gamma!}$ is non-zero, then

$$J_\gamma(\rho)=\frac{\rho^\gamma}{2^\gamma \gamma!}(1+0(\rho^2)) \quad \text{as} \quad \rho \to 0. \tag{69}$$

Since $s!$ is non-zero for all s (s is either zero or a positive integer), a coefficient of a term in equation (68) is zero only if $(\gamma+s)!$ is infinite. But $(\gamma+s)!$ is infinite only if $\gamma+s$ is a negative integer. Consequently equation (69) is valid except when γ is a negative integer. Since ρ^n and ρ^{-n} are linearly independent, J_n and J_{-n} are linearly independent whenever n is not an integer.

If γ is a negative integer, $-n$ say, then $\dfrac{1}{(-n+s)!}=0$ for $s=0, 1, 2, \ldots, n-1$ and

$$J_{-n}(\rho)=\sum_{s=n}^{\infty} \frac{(-)^s}{s!(-n+s)!}\left(\frac{\rho}{2}\right)^{-n+2s}.$$

† See J. A. Green, *Sequences and Series*, uniform with this volume.

Put $s-n=t$, then

$$J_{-n}(\rho)=\sum_{t=0}^{\infty}\frac{(-)^{n}(-)^{t}}{(t+n)!\,t!}\left(\frac{\rho}{2}\right)^{n+2t}=(-)^{n}J_{n}(\rho) \text{ for } n \text{ integral;}$$

$$(70)$$

i.e. $J_{-n}(\rho)$ and $J_{n}(\rho)$ are linearly dependent whenever n is an integer and therefore there are solutions of Bessel's equation of integral order n not expressible as a linear combination of these two functions.

2. BESSEL FUNCTIONS OF THE SECOND KIND

The result at the end of the last section presents the problem of finding a solution of Bessel's equation of integral order n which is linearly independent of J_{n}. Such a solution can be constructed in the following manner. Define $Y_{q}(\rho)$ by

$$Y_{q}(\rho)=\frac{J_{q}(\rho)\cos q\pi-J_{-q}(\rho)}{\sin q\pi}. \qquad (71)$$

When q is not an integer, $Y_{q}(\rho)$ is a linear combination of two solutions of Bessel's equation and is itself a solution. The value $Y_{n}(\rho)$, n integral, cannot be obtained by substituting $q=n$ into equation (71) because this gives $0/0$, which is indeterminate. As is usual in these circumstances, the value of $Y_{n}(\rho)$ must be obtained by differentiation of numerator and denominator with respect to q, using equation (68) for J_{q} and J_{-q}, and then putting $q=n$. The details of the algebra are complicated. The final result is

$$Y_{n}(\rho)=\frac{2}{\pi}J_{n}(\rho)\ln \rho/2-\frac{1}{\pi}\sum_{r=0}^{\infty}(-)^{r}\frac{(\rho/2)^{n+2r}}{r!(n+r)!}\{\mathbf{F}(r)+\mathbf{F}(n+r)\}$$

$$-\frac{1}{\pi}\sum_{r=0}^{n-1}\frac{(n-r-1)!}{r!}\left(\frac{\rho}{2}\right)^{-n+2r} \qquad (72)$$

where $\mathbf{F}(r)$, known as the digamma function, is given by

$$\mathbf{F}(r) = \frac{\mathrm{d}}{\mathrm{d}r}(\ln r!)$$

$$= \lim_{n \to \infty} \left(\ln n - \frac{1}{r+1} - \frac{1}{r+2} - \frac{1}{r+3} - \dots - \frac{1}{r+n} \right), \quad (73)$$

and ln denotes a logarithm to base e.

When n is a positive integer, $Y_n(\rho)$ has a singularity of the same order as ρ^{-n} at $\rho = 0$; when n is zero, the singularity is logarithmic. Since $J_n(\rho)$, $n \geqslant 0$, is finite at the origin, $Y_n(\rho)$ and $J_n(\rho)$ are linearly independent and any solution of Bessel's equation of order n is expressible as a linear combination of $J_n(\rho)$ and $Y_n(\rho)$. $Y_n(\rho)$ is known as a Bessel function of the second kind.

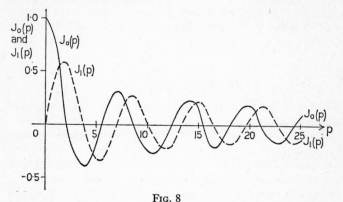

FIG. 8

$J_0(p)$ and $J_1(p)$ are plotted against p in the above figure. Note that they oscillate with decreasing amplitude as p increases.

Tables† of $J_n(\rho)$ and $Y_n(\rho)$ have been constructed for the commonly occurring values of n and ρ. With such tables it is no more difficult to evaluate an expression containing a Bessel function than one containing a trigonometric function.

† E.g. E. Jahnke and F. Emde, *Tables of Functions*, Dover, New York.

3. DERIVATIVES OF BESSEL FUNCTIONS AND RECURRENCE FORMULAE

Let us find the derivatives with respect to ρ of the Bessel function of the first kind

$$J_n(\rho) = \sum_{s=0}^{\infty} \frac{(-)^s}{s!\,(n+s)!} \left(\frac{\rho}{2}\right)^{n+2s} ; \qquad (68)$$

n can be either integral or non-integral. Carry out the differentiation and multiply both sides by ρ:

$$\rho J_n'(\rho) = \sum_{s=0}^{\infty} \frac{(-)^s\,(n+2s)}{s!\,(n+s)!} \left(\frac{\rho}{2}\right)^{n+2s} \qquad (74)$$

$$= n \sum_{s=0}^{\infty} \frac{(-)^s}{s!\,(n+s)!} \left(\frac{\rho}{2}\right)^{n+2s}$$

$$+ \rho \sum_{s=1}^{\infty} \frac{(-)^s}{(s-1)!\,(n+s)!} \left(\frac{\rho}{2}\right)^{n+2s-1}$$

The first sum is equal to $J_n(\rho)$. Put $s-1=r$ in the second sum:

$$\rho J_n'(\rho) = n J_n(\rho) - \rho \sum_{r=0}^{\infty} \frac{(-)^r}{r!\,(n+1+r)!} \left(\frac{\rho}{2}\right)^{n+1-2r} ,$$

i.e.

$$\rho J_n'(\rho) = n J_n(\rho) - \rho J_{n+1}(\rho). \qquad (75)$$

Alternatively from equation (74)

$$\rho J_n'(\rho) = \rho \sum_{s=0}^{\infty} \frac{(-)^s}{s!\,(n+s-1)!} \left(\frac{\rho}{2}\right)^{n+2s-1}$$

$$- n \sum_{s=0}^{\infty} \frac{(-)^s}{s!\,(n+s)!} \left(\frac{\rho}{2}\right)^{n+2s} ,$$

i.e.

$$\rho J_n'(\rho) = \rho J_{n-1}(\rho) - n J_n(\rho). \qquad (76)$$

Adding equations (75) and (76),

$$J_n{}'(\rho) = \tfrac{1}{2}(J_{n-1}(\rho) - J_{n+1}(\rho)). \tag{77}$$

Subtracting equation (75) from equation (76),

$$2nJ_n(\rho) = \rho(J_{n-1}(\rho) + J_{n+1}(\rho)). \tag{78}$$

Equations (75), (76) and (77) are alternative expressions for the derivative of the Bessel function of the first kind with respect to its argument. Equation (78) is a recurrence relation; it shows that a linear relation exists between three successive Bessel functions for a succession in which the order of the function is increased by unity at each step.

The Bessel function of the second kind $Y_n(\rho)$ satisfies equations identical to equations (75) to (78) except that $J_n(\rho)$ is replaced by $Y_n(\rho)$. Let us prove the analogue of equation (75) for integral n. From equation (71),

$$Y_n(\rho) = \lim_{q \to n} \frac{J_q(\rho) \cos q\pi - J_{-q}(\rho)}{\sin q\pi}.$$

$$\therefore \quad \rho Y_n{}'(\rho) = \rho \lim_{q \to n} \frac{J_q{}'(\rho) \cos q\pi - J_{-q}{}'(\rho)}{\sin q\pi}.$$

Using equation (75) for $J_q'(\rho)$ and equation (76) for $J_{-q}'(\rho)$,

$$\rho Y_n{}'(\rho)$$

$$= \rho \lim_{q \to n} \frac{\left(\dfrac{q}{\rho}J_q(\rho) - J_{q+1}(\rho)\right)\cos q\pi - \left(J_{-q-1}(\rho) + \dfrac{q}{\rho}J_{-q}(\rho)\right)}{\sin q\pi}$$

$$= \lim_{q \to n} q\frac{J_q(\rho) \cos q\pi - J_{-q}(\rho)}{\sin q\pi}$$

$$\quad - \rho \lim_{q \to n} \frac{J_{q+1}(\rho) \cos(q+1)\pi - J_{-q-1}(\rho)}{\sin(q+1)\pi},$$

since $\cos q\pi = -\cos(q+1)\pi$ and $\sin q\pi = -\sin(q+1)\pi$. Hence, on use of equation (71),

$$\rho Y_n{}'(\rho) = nY_n(\rho) - \rho Y_{n+1}(\rho). \tag{79}$$

Exercise 6

Show that $\rho Y_n{}'(\rho) = \rho Y_{n-1}(\rho) + n Y_n(\rho)$. (80)

Hence, from equations (79) and (80) or otherwise, show that

$$Y_n{}'(\rho) = \tfrac{1}{2}(Y_{n-1}(\rho) - Y_{n+1}(\rho)) \tag{81}$$

and

$$2n Y_n(\rho) = \rho(Y_{n-1}(\rho) + Y_{n+1}(\rho)). \tag{82}$$

Important special cases of equations (75) to (82) are

$$J_0{}'(\rho) = -J_1(\rho), \ \ Y_0{}'(\rho) = -Y_1(\rho), \tag{83}$$

$$J_1{}'(\rho) = J_0(\rho) - \frac{1}{\rho} J_1(\rho) \ \text{and} \ Y_1{}'(\rho) = Y_0(\rho) - \frac{1}{\rho} Y_1(\rho). \tag{84}$$

We shall require later the following result, which is derived from equations (83) and (84):

$$\frac{\mathrm{d}}{\mathrm{d}\rho}\left[\rho^2\left(J_0{}^2(\rho) + J_1{}^2(\rho)\right)\right]$$

$$= 2\rho(J_0{}^2 + J_1{}^2) + \rho^2 2J_0(-J_1) + \rho^2 2J_1\left(J_0 - \frac{1}{\rho} J_1\right)$$

$$= 2\rho J_0{}^2(\rho). \tag{85}$$

Exercise 7

For arbitrary n, show that

$$\frac{d}{d\rho}\{\rho^2[J_n{}^2(\rho) - J_{n-1}(\rho)J_{n+1}(\rho)]\} = 2\rho J_n{}^2(\rho).$$

4. MODIFIED BESSEL FUNCTIONS

We now consider $a < 0$ in equation (43). If we again put

$$\rho = \sqrt{a}\,r, \tag{53}$$

then ρ is complex. But the analysis in section 1 is unaltered and we again derive $J_n(\rho)$ and $J_{-n}(\rho)$ as solutions of equation (43) where

$$J_\gamma(\rho) = \sum_{s=0}^{\infty} \frac{(-)^s}{s!\,(\gamma+s)!}\left(\frac{\rho}{2}\right)^{\gamma+2s}. \tag{68}$$

Since $a < 0$, put $\sigma = \sqrt{-a}\,r$ and σ will be real. Then $\rho = i\sigma$ and

$$J_\gamma(i\sigma) = i^\gamma \sum_{s=0}^{\infty} \frac{1}{s! \, (\gamma+s)!} \left(\frac{\sigma}{2}\right)^{\gamma+2s} \tag{69}$$

Note

$$i^\gamma = (e^{i\pi/2})^\gamma = \cos\frac{\gamma\pi}{2} + i\sin\frac{\gamma\pi}{2}.$$

It can be seen from equation (69) that $i^{-\gamma}J_\gamma(i\sigma)$ is real. We therefore define $I_\gamma(\sigma)$ as $i^{-\gamma}J_\gamma(i\sigma)$. From equation (69),

$$I_\gamma(\sigma) = \sum_{s=0}^{\infty} \frac{1}{s! \, (\gamma+s)!} \left(\frac{\sigma}{2}\right)^{\gamma+2s}. \tag{86}$$

$J_\gamma(\rho)$ satisfies equation (54) with $n^2 = \gamma^2$. Substituting $\rho = i\sigma$ in this equation, the equation satisfied by $J_\gamma(i\sigma)$ is found to be

$$\frac{d^2R}{d\sigma^2} + \frac{1}{\sigma}\frac{dR}{d\sigma} - \left(1 + \frac{n^2}{\sigma^2}\right)R = 0. \tag{87}$$

$I_\gamma(\sigma)$ is a constant multiple of $J_\gamma(i\sigma)$ and so $I_\gamma(\sigma)$ satisfies equation (87). But $\gamma = \pm n$ and therefore $I_n(\sigma)$ and $I_{-n}(\sigma)$ are two solutions of equation (87). Equation (87) is known as the modified Bessel's equation for functions of order n and the function $I_\gamma(\sigma)$ is known as a modified Bessel function of the first kind. It is said to be of order γ. Sometimes $I_\gamma(\sigma)$ is called a 'Bessel function of the first kind with imaginary argument'. Note that equation (87) can be derived directly from equation (43) by the substitution $\sigma = \sqrt{-a}r$.

$I_n(\sigma)$ and $I_{-n}(\sigma)$ are linearly independent solutions of equation (87) except when n is an integer. We define $K_q(\sigma)$ by

$$K_q(\sigma) = \{I_{-q}(\sigma) - I_q(\sigma)\}/\tan q\pi. \tag{88}$$

If q is not an integer, $K_q(\sigma)$ is a linear combination of two solutions of the modified Bessel's equation and is itself a solution. When q is an integer, substitution of $q = n$ in the right-hand side of equation (88) gives $0/0$. Therefore numerator and denominator must be differentiated with respect to q before substitution of $q=n$. This can be shown to give

$$K_n(\sigma)$$
$$= -\frac{2}{\pi} I_n(\sigma) \ln \frac{\sigma}{2} + \frac{1}{\pi} \sum_{r=0}^{\infty} \frac{(\sigma/2)^{n+2r}}{r!(n+r)!} \{\mathbf{F}(r) + \mathbf{F}(n+r)\}$$

$$+ \frac{1}{\pi} \sum_{r=0}^{\infty} \frac{(-)^{n-r}(n-r+1)!}{r!} \left(\frac{\sigma}{2}\right)^{-n+2r}, \qquad (89)$$

where $\mathbf{F}(r)$ is given by equation (73). $I_n(\sigma)$ and $K_n(\sigma)$ are two linearly independent solutions of the modified Bessel equation of order n. $K_n(\sigma)$ is known as a modified Bessel function of the second kind.

Derivatives of and recurrence relations for the I_n can be obtained from equations (75) to (78). Substitute $\rho = i\sigma$ in equation (75) and put $J_\gamma(i\sigma) = i^\gamma I_\gamma(\sigma)$:

$$i\sigma \frac{d}{d(i\sigma)} \left(i^n I_n(\sigma) \right) = n i^n I_n(\sigma) - i\sigma \, i^{n+1} I_{n+1}(\sigma),$$
$$\sigma I_n'(\sigma) = n I_n(\sigma) + \sigma I_{n+1}(\sigma). \qquad (90)$$

Similarly from equation (76),

$$i\sigma \frac{d}{d(i\sigma)} \left(i^n I_n(\sigma) \right) = i\sigma \, i^{n-1} I_{n-1}(\sigma) - n i^n I_n(\sigma),$$
$$\sigma I_n'(\sigma) = \sigma I_{n-1}(\sigma) - n I_n(\sigma). \qquad (91)$$

Adding and subtracting equations (90) and (91),

$$I_n'(\sigma) = \tfrac{1}{2}(I_{n-1}(\sigma) + I_{n+1}(\sigma)) \qquad (92)$$

and

$$2n I_n(\sigma) = \sigma(I_{n-1}(\sigma) - I_{n+1}(\sigma)). \qquad (93)$$

Exercise 8

(i) Show that $I_{-n}(\sigma) = I_n(\sigma)$ when n is a positive integer.
(ii) Show that $K_n(\sigma)$ satisfies the same recurrence relations as $I_n(\sigma)$.
Hint: Use the method employed to derive equation (79).

Important special cases of the derivative formulae are

$$I_0'(\sigma) = I_1(\sigma), \; K_0'(\sigma) = K_1(\sigma), \qquad (94)$$

$$I_1'(\sigma) = I_0(\sigma) - \frac{1}{\sigma} I_1(\sigma), \; K_1'(\sigma) = K_0(\sigma) - \frac{1}{\sigma} K_1(\sigma). \qquad (95)$$

5. BEHAVIOUR OF BESSEL FUNCTIONS AT ZERO AND INFINITY

The principal term as the argument of the Bessel function tends to zero can be found from equations (68), (72), (86) and (89). Equations (68) and (86) show that both $J_n(\rho)$ and $I_n(\rho)$ equal $\dfrac{1}{n!}\left(\dfrac{\rho}{2}\right)^n\left(1+\mathrm{O}(\rho^2)\right)$ as $\rho\to0$ provided n is not a negative integer, therefore

$$J_n(\rho) \text{ and } I_n(\rho) \xrightarrow[\rho\to0]{} \begin{cases} 0 & \text{if } n>0 \\ 1 & \text{if } n=0 \\ \infty & \text{if } n<0 \text{ but non-integral.} \end{cases}$$

Equations (72) and (89) show that, for n a positive integer,

$$Y_n(\rho)= -\frac{1}{\pi}(n-1)!\left(\frac{\rho}{2}\right)^{-n}\left(1+\mathrm{O}(\rho^2)\right) \text{ as } \rho\to0,$$

therefore $Y_n(\rho) \xrightarrow[\rho\to0]{} \infty$;

and $\qquad K_n(\rho)=(-)^n\dfrac{1}{\pi}(n-1)!\left(\dfrac{\rho}{2}\right)^{-n}\left(1+\mathrm{O}(\rho^2)\right)$ as $\rho\to0,$

therefore $K_n(\rho) \xrightarrow[\rho\to0]{} \infty.$

Also, for $n=0$,

$$Y_0(\rho)=\frac{2}{\pi}\ln\rho-\frac{2}{\pi}\left(\ln2+\mathbf{F}(0)\right)+\mathrm{O}(\rho^2) \text{ as } \rho\to0,$$

therefore $Y_0(\rho) \xrightarrow[\rho\to0]{} -\infty$;

and $\qquad K_0(\rho)= -\dfrac{2}{\pi}\ln\rho+\dfrac{2}{\pi}\left(\ln2+\mathbf{F}(0)\right)+\mathrm{O}(\rho^2)$ as $\rho\to0,$

therefore $K_0(\rho) \xrightarrow[\rho\to0]{} \infty$

Note that, whatever the value of n, both for Bessel's equation and for the modified Bessel equation, there is one solution which remains finite and one solution which becomes infinite as the argument tends to zero.

To determine the behaviour of the Bessel functions as their arguments tends to infinity (through real values), we first eliminate the term involving the first derivative in equation (54) by the substitution $R(\rho)=\rho^{-\frac{1}{2}} S(\rho)$. The reader can verify that equation (54) becomes

$$\frac{d^2 S}{d\rho^2}+\left(1+\frac{1/4-n^2}{\rho^2}\right)S=0.$$

For large ρ, the term in $1/\rho^2$ can be neglected compared to 1 and this suggests that $S(\rho)$ behaves like $\sin \rho$ or $\cos \rho$ as $\rho \to \infty$. This argument can be made rigorous. Therefore $R(\rho)=\rho^{-\frac{1}{2}} S(\rho)$ behaves like $\rho^{-\frac{1}{2}} \sin \rho$ or $\rho^{-\frac{1}{2}} \cos \rho$ as $\rho \to \infty$. But $J_n(\rho)$ with either $J_{-n}(\rho)$ or $Y_n(\rho)$ are the solutions of equation (54). Therefore these Bessel functions tend to zero like $\rho^{-\frac{1}{2}} \begin{smallmatrix} \sin \\ \cos \end{smallmatrix} \rho$ as $\rho \to \infty$.

If we make the substitution $R(\sigma)=\sigma^{-\frac{1}{2}} S(\sigma)$ in equation (87),

$$\frac{d^2 S}{d\sigma^2}+\left(-1+\frac{1/4-n^2}{\sigma^2}\right)S=0.$$

As before, it is inferred that $S(\rho)$ behaves like e^{σ} or $e^{-\sigma}$ as $\rho \to \infty$. This can be proved rigorously. Therefore $R(\sigma)$ behaves either like $\sigma^{-\frac{1}{2}} e^{\sigma}$ or like $\sigma^{-\frac{1}{2}} e^{-\sigma}$ as $\sigma \to \infty$. One independent solution of equation (87) tends to infinity, the other tends to zero as $\sigma \to \infty$. Since all terms, except the first few if $\gamma < -1$, in the sum on the right-hand side of equation (86) have positive coefficients, $I_n(\sigma) \to \infty$ as $\sigma \to \infty$. It can be shown by methods beyond the scope of this book that $K_n(\sigma)$ is the solution of equation (87) that tends to zero as $\sigma \to \infty$ for n both integral and non-integral.

6. SERIES OF ZERO ORDER BESSEL FUNCTIONS

It is well known that in an interval, $0 \leqslant r \leqslant R$ many functions of r can be expanded as infinite series of either sines or cosines. These series are known as Fourier sine and Fourier cosine series respectively. It is also possible to expand functions of r as infinite series of Bessel functions all of the same order. In this section, for simplicity, we shall consider expansion in terms of Bessel functions of zero order. This is the most important case in practice as it arises in problems with axial symmetry (see e.g. chapter 4, section 4).

In Fourier series the arguments of all terms are integral multiples of the argument of the first term; i.e. $\dfrac{n\pi r}{R}$, the argument of the n'th term sin or cos $\dfrac{n\pi r}{R}$, is an integral multiple of $\dfrac{\pi r}{R}$, the argument of the first term sin or cos $\dfrac{\pi r}{R}$. This is not the case with expansions in Bessel functions. However, the arguments $\dfrac{n\pi r}{R}$ can be considered as the values of kr for which sin $kr=0$ at $r=R$; in the case of the cosine series, values of k are chosen such that the derivative of each term is zero at $r=R$. This suggests that we look for expansions in terms of zero order Bessel functions $J_0(kr)$ where the values of k are chosen such that either $J_0(kr)=0$ at $r=R$ or $J_0'(kr)=0$ at $r=R$. We can solve both problems together if we take the condition as

$$\alpha J_0(kr)+\beta kr J_0'(kr)=0 \text{ at } r=R, \qquad (96)$$

and later put one of the constants α or β equal to zero. We now assume† that $f(r)$, known in the interval $0\leqslant r\leqslant R$, can be expanded as an infinite series of the form

$$f(r)=\sum_{n=1}^{\infty}B_n J_0(k_n r) \text{ for } 0\leqslant r\leqslant R, \qquad (97)$$

where k_1, k_2, k_3, etc., are the roots of equation (96) arranged in ascending order of magnitude.‡ The problem is to find

† The problems involved in justifying this assumption are very difficult, see G. N. Watson, *A Treatise on the Theory of Bessel Functions*, Chapter 18, 2nd edit. Cambridge University Press, 1944.

‡ It can be shown that the k_n are all distinct and positive, except for $\alpha=0$ when $k_1=0$. The values of $k_n R$ for $\beta=0$ are the zeros of $J_0(x)$, for $\alpha=0$ the zeros of $J_1(x)$. These zeros are well tabulated.

the values of the constant coefficients B_n.

To find the coefficient of the term $\sin \dfrac{n\pi r}{R}$ in the Fourier sine series, one multiplied through by $\sin \dfrac{m\pi r}{R}$ and integrated from 0 to R. This method worked because $\int_0^R \sin \dfrac{n\pi r}{R} \sin \dfrac{m\pi r}{R} \, dr$ is zero when $n \neq m$. In the case of equation (97) we shall multiply through by $rJ_0(k_m r)$ and integrate from 0 to R, because, as will be shown immediately

$$\int_0^R rJ_0(k_n r) J_0(k_m r) \, dr = 0 \quad \text{when } n \neq m. \tag{98}$$

Equation (54) can be written

$$\frac{d}{d\rho}\left(\rho R'(\rho)\right) + \rho R(\rho) = 0.$$

But $J_0(\rho)$ satisfies equation (54). Therefore, putting $\rho = k_n r$,

$$\frac{d}{dr}\left(rJ_0'(k_n r)\right) + k_n r J_0(k_n r) = 0. \tag{99}$$

Multiply equation (99) by $J_0(k_m r)$, $m \neq n$, and integrate with respect to r from 0 to R:

$$\int_0^R J_0(k_m r)\frac{d}{dr}\left(rJ_0'(k_n r)\right)dr + k_n \int_0^R rJ_0(k_m r)J_0(k_n r)dr = 0.$$

$$\therefore k_n \int_0^R rJ_0(k_m r)J_0(k_n r)dr = -RJ_0(k_m R)J_0'(k_n R)$$

$$+ \int_0^R rJ_0'(k_n r)k_m J_0'(k_m r)dr, \tag{100}$$

on integration by parts and use of

$$\frac{d}{dr} J_0(k_m r) = k_m \frac{d}{d(k_m r)} J_0(k_m r) = k_m J_0'(k_m r).$$

If n and m are interchanged in equation (100),

$$k_m \int_0^R rJ_0(k_n r)J_0(k_m r)dr$$

$$= -RJ_0(k_nR)J_0'(k_mR) + \int_0^R rJ_0'(k_mr)k_nJ_0'(k_nr)\mathrm{d}r. \quad (101)$$

Multiply equation (100) by k_n, equation (101) by k_m and subtract:

$$(k_n{}^2 - k_m{}^2)\int_0^R rJ_0(k_nr)J_0(k_mr)\mathrm{d}r \qquad (102)$$
$$= k_mRJ_0'(k_mR)J_0(k_nR) - k_nRJ_0'(k_nR)J_0(k_mR).$$

Since both k_n and k_m satisfy equation (96), the right-hand side of equation (102) is zero. Therefore, since $k_n \neq k_m$,

$$\int_0^R rJ_0(k_nr)J_0(k_mr)\mathrm{d}r = 0. \qquad (98)$$

It follows from equation (85) that

$$\int_0^\omega \rho J_0{}^2(\rho)\ \mathrm{d}\rho = \frac{\omega^2}{2}\{J_0{}^2(\omega) + J_1{}^2(\omega)\},$$

where ω is any positive number.
Putting $\rho = k_mr$ and $\omega = k_mR$,

$$\int_0^R rJ_0{}^2(k_mr)\ \mathrm{d}r = \frac{R^2}{2}\{J_0{}^2(k_mR) + J_1{}^2(k_mR)\}. \quad (103)$$

Now multiply equation (97) through by $rJ_0(k_mr)$ and integrate from 0 to R.† By equation (98) all terms in the infinite sum, for which $n \neq m$, vanish. In the remaining term substitute from equation (103); whence

$$\int_0^R f(r)rJ_0(k_mr)\mathrm{d}r = B_m\frac{R^2}{2}\{J_0{}^2(k_mR) + J_1{}^2(k_mR)\}.$$

Therefore

$$B_n = \frac{2\int_0^R f(r)rJ_0(k_nr)\mathrm{d}r}{R^2\{J_0{}^2(k_nR) + J_1{}^2(k_nR)\}}. \qquad (104)$$

Equations (97) and (104) enable many functions of r to be expressed as infinite series of Bessel functions of zero order

† It is assumed that this process is legitimate.

in the interval $0 \leqslant r \leqslant R$. The practical value of this result will be seen in the next chapter.

Exercise 9

Show that $e^{\frac{1}{2}\rho(t-1/t)} = \sum_{n=-\infty}^{\infty} t^n J_n(\rho)$. Because of this property $e^{\frac{1}{2}\rho(t-1/t)}$ is known as the 'generating function' for Bessel functions.

Hint: Expand the exponential, then expand the powers of $(t - \frac{1}{t})$ and finally collect powers of t^n together.

CHAPTER FOUR

Solutions Using Cylindrical Polar Co-ordinates

---

1. FORM OF SOLUTIONS OF LAPLACE'S EQUATION

In chapter 2, section 4, we looked for solutions of Laplace's equation in cylindrical polar co-ordinates r, θ, z of the form

$$\phi = R(r)\,\Theta(\theta)\,Z(z), \qquad (40)$$

and we found in chapter 3 that the form of the solution depended upon the values of the constants a and n. We can summarize the results as follows:

(i) $a=0$, $n>0$,

$$\phi = r^{\pm n}\begin{pmatrix}\cos \\ \sin\end{pmatrix}n\theta\begin{pmatrix}1 \\ z\end{pmatrix}, \qquad (105)$$

where the right-hand side of equation (105) is shorthand for the linear combination of all the possible values for ϕ that are shown; i.e.

$$\phi = Ar^n \cos n\theta + Br^n \sin n\theta + Cr^{-n} \cos n\theta + Dr^{-n} \sin n\theta$$
$$+ Er^n z \cos n\theta + Fr^n z \sin n\theta + Gr^{-n} \cos n\theta + Hr^{-n} z \sin n\theta.$$

(ii) $a=0$, $n=0$,

$$\phi = \begin{pmatrix}1 \\ \ln r\end{pmatrix}\begin{pmatrix}1 \\ \theta\end{pmatrix}\begin{pmatrix}1 \\ z\end{pmatrix}. \qquad (106)$$

(iii) $a>0$, $n>0$ but non-integral,

$$\phi = J_{\pm n}(\sqrt{a}\,r)\begin{pmatrix}\cos \\ \sin\end{pmatrix}n\theta\; e^{\pm\sqrt{a}\,z}. \qquad (107)$$

(iv) $a>0$, $n>0$,

$$\phi = \frac{J_n}{Y_n}(\sqrt{a}\,r)\begin{pmatrix}\cos \\ \sin\end{pmatrix}n\theta\; e^{\pm\sqrt{a}\,z}. \qquad (108)$$

(v) $a > 0$, $n = 0$,

$$\phi = \frac{J_0}{Y_0}(\sqrt{a}r) \begin{pmatrix} 1 \\ \theta \end{pmatrix} e^{\pm\sqrt{a}z}. \tag{109}$$

(vi) $a < 0$, $n > 0$ but non-integral,

$$\phi = I_{\pm n}(\sqrt{-a}r) \begin{pmatrix} \cos \\ \sin \end{pmatrix} n\theta \begin{pmatrix} \cos \\ \sin \end{pmatrix} \sqrt{-a}z. \tag{110}$$

(vii) $a < 0$, $n > 0$,

$$\phi = \frac{I_n}{K_n}(\sqrt{-a}r) \begin{pmatrix} \cos \\ \sin \end{pmatrix} n\theta \begin{pmatrix} \cos \\ \sin \end{pmatrix} \sqrt{-a}z. \tag{111}$$

(viii) $a < 0$, $n = 0$,

$$\phi = \frac{I_0}{K_0}(\sqrt{-a}\,r) \begin{pmatrix} 1 \\ \theta \end{pmatrix} \begin{pmatrix} \cos \\ \sin \end{pmatrix} \sqrt{-a}\,z. \tag{112}$$

There are other solutions which arise from a and/or n being complex numbers. These solutions, however, are beyond the scope of this book.

The behaviour of the different functions at zero and infinity frequently narrows the choice of solutions in a given problem. Suppose that we insist that ϕ must be finite for all values of the independent variables which occur in a particular case. Then if the range of the independent variables r and z includes $r = 0$ and $z \to +\infty$ and if we wish to try a solution of the form of equation (108), the only permitted solutions would be of the form

$$\phi = J_n(\sqrt{a}r) \begin{pmatrix} \cos \\ \sin \end{pmatrix} n\theta \, e^{-\sqrt{a}z};$$

terms containing $Y_n(\sqrt{a}r)$ are excluded because $Y_n(\rho) \to \infty$ as $\rho \to 0$ (see chapter 3, section 5) and terms containing $e^{\sqrt{a}z}$ are excluded because $e^{\sqrt{a}z} \to \infty$ as $z \to \infty$.

2. AN INFINITE CYLINDER IN A UNIFORM FIELD

An infinite right circular cylinder is placed in a uniformly flowing liquid so that the axis of the cylinder makes an angle $\frac{\pi}{2}-\alpha$ with the direction of the uniform flow. The problem is to determine the velocity field in the presence of the cylinder.

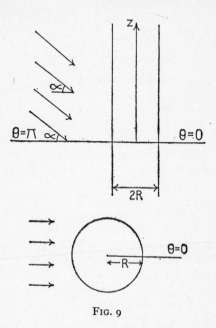

FIG. 9

Choose the z-axis along the axis of the cylinder and the plane, in which the z-axis and the uniform flow velocity vectors lie, as $\theta=0$. Let the radius of the cylinder be R. Since the presence of the cylinder will have decreasing effect as distance from the cylinder increases, we shall look for a velocity field which tends to the velocity field of uniform flow as $r\rightarrow\infty$. Since no flow takes place across the surface of the cylinder, the component of the velocity normal to the surface must be zero, i.e. $v_r=0$ at $r=R$.

Let us first consider the case $\alpha=0$ illustrated in the lower

50

diagram. Now the problem is effectively two-dimensional as there is no dependence on z. The velocity as $r \to \infty$ tends to be parallel to the line $\theta = 0$. In Cartesian co-ordinates this implies a velocity potential ϕ tending to $V_0 x$ where V_0 is the speed of uniform flow. In polar co-ordinates the velocity potential tends to $V_0 r \cos \theta$ since $x = r \cos \theta$. The velocity potential $V_0 r \cos \theta$ satisfies Laplace's equation, see equation (105), but at $r = R$ it gives $\dfrac{\partial \phi}{\partial r} = V_0 \cos \theta \neq 0$. It is necessary to add to $V_0 r \cos \theta$ a term with the following properties: (i) that it satisfies Laplace's equation; (ii) that its partial derivative with respect to r at $r = R$ is equal to $-V_0 \cos \theta$ and (iii) that its spacial derivatives tend to zero as $r \to \infty$. For condition (ii) to be satisfied the term added must be of the form $f(r) \cos \theta$ where $f'(r) = -V_0$ at $r = R$. Condition (i) and equation (105) determine any possible $f(r)$ to be of the form $f(r) = \dfrac{A}{r} \cos \theta$ where A is a constant. For $f'(r) = -V_0$ at $r = R$, $A = R^2 V_0$ and $f(r) = \dfrac{R^2 V_0}{r}$. The spacial derivatives are of order $\dfrac{1}{r^2}$ as $r \to \infty$ and therefore condition (iii) is satisfied. All the conditions of the problem are satisfied and the velocity potential is

$$\phi = V_0 \left(r + \frac{R^2}{r} \right) \cos \theta. \tag{113}$$

The velocity components are

$$v_r = \frac{\partial \phi}{\partial r} = V_0 \left(1 - \frac{R^2}{r^2} \right) \cos \theta,$$

$$v_\theta = \frac{1}{r} \frac{\partial \phi}{\partial \theta} = -V_0 \left(1 + \frac{R^2}{r^2} \right) \sin \theta$$

and

$$v_z = \frac{\partial \phi}{\partial z} = 0.$$

When $\alpha \neq 0$, we split the flow at infinity into two components, the one of magnitude $V_0 \cos \alpha$ normal to the axis of the cylinder and the other of magnitude $V_0 \sin \alpha$ parallel to the axis of the cylinder. The former flow is the one we have just considered and the latter flow is unaffected by the presence of the cylinder. The velocity potential and components of velocity are therefore

$$\phi = V_0 \cos \alpha \left(r + \frac{R^2}{r} \right) \cos \theta + z \, V_0 \sin \alpha,$$

$$v_r = \frac{\partial \phi}{\partial r} = V_0 \cos \alpha \left(1 - \frac{R^2}{r^2} \right) \cos \theta,$$

$$v_\theta = \frac{1}{r} \frac{\partial \phi}{\partial \theta} = - V_0 \cos \alpha \left(1 + \frac{R^2}{r^2} \right) \sin \theta$$

and

$$v_z = \frac{\partial \phi}{\partial z} = V_0 \sin \alpha.$$

Note that the effect of the cylinder on the velocity field falls off as $\dfrac{1}{r^2}$ outside the cylinder.

3. A PARTICULAR SOLID OF REVOLUTION IN A UNIFORM FIELD

The particular solid chosen is obtained by varying the

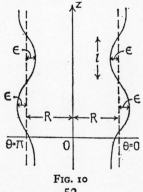

FIG. 10

radius of the cylinder of the previous example sinusoidally with z, i.e. the surface of the cylinder is given by

$$r = R\left(1 + \epsilon \sin \frac{z\pi}{l}\right). \tag{114}$$

ϵ is sufficiently small compared to 1 to enable squares of ϵ to be neglected compared to 1, and R and l are of the same order of magnitude. The solid is a solid of revolution of which each cross-section normal to the z-axis is a circle. The undisturbed velocity is normal to the z-axis.

Since ϵ is small, a first approximation to the velocity potential will be given by equation (113). Equation (113) satisfies the conditions at infinity, i.e. flow identical to the flow in the absence of the solid, and it also satisfies Laplace's equation. There remains the boundary condition on the surface of the solid that the component of velocity normal to the surface, v_n, should be zero. If ψ is the angle between the tangent to the surface in the r, z plane and the z-axis, then

$$v_n = v_r \cos \psi - v_z \sin \psi$$
$$= \frac{\partial \phi}{\partial r} \cos \psi - \frac{\partial \phi}{\partial z} \sin \psi.$$

Fig. 11

Now $\tan \psi = \dfrac{\mathrm{d}r}{\mathrm{d}z} = \dfrac{R\epsilon\pi}{l} \cos \dfrac{z\pi}{l}$,

on using equation (114). Since $\dfrac{R\epsilon\pi}{l}$ is of order ϵ,

$$\sin\psi = \frac{R\epsilon\pi}{l}\cos\frac{z\pi}{l} + O(\epsilon^3) \text{ and } \cos\psi = 1 + O(\epsilon^2).$$

The boundary condition becomes

$$v_n = \frac{\partial\phi}{\partial r} - \frac{R\epsilon\pi}{l}\cos\frac{z\pi}{l}\frac{\partial\phi}{\partial z} = 0, \tag{115}$$

whenever

$$r = R\left(1 + \epsilon\sin\frac{z\pi}{l}\right). \tag{114}$$

Substituting from equation (113), v_n equals $V_0\left(1 - \frac{R^2}{r^2}\right)\cos\theta$ since $\frac{\partial\phi}{\partial z} = 0$. Therefore, when $r = R\left(1 + \epsilon\sin\frac{z\pi}{l}\right)$,

$$v_n = V_0\left(1 - \left\{1 + \epsilon\sin\frac{z\pi}{l}\right\}^{-2}\right)\cos\theta = 2V_0\epsilon\sin\frac{z\pi}{l}\cos\theta.$$

Equation (115) is not satisfied.

It is necessary to add another term to the right-hand side of equation (113). This term must satisfy Laplace's equation and have vanishing spacial derivatives at infinity. The only functions containing $\sin\frac{z\pi}{l}$ and $\cos\theta$ as factors which occur in equations (105) to (112) are $I_1\left(\frac{\pi r}{l}\right)\cos\theta\sin\frac{\pi z}{l}$ and $K_1\left(\frac{\pi r}{l}\right)\cos\theta\sin\frac{\pi z}{l}$. But $I_1(\sigma)\to\infty$ as $\sigma\to\infty$ and $K_1(\sigma)\to 0$ as $\sigma\to\infty$, therefore the only term we can add to the right-hand side of equation (113) is a constant of order ϵ times $K_1\left(\frac{\pi r}{l}\right)\cos\theta\sin\frac{\pi z}{l}$; i.e. we now try as velocity potential

$$\phi = V_0\cos\theta\left\{r + \frac{R^2}{r} + AK_1\left(\frac{\pi r}{l}\right)\sin\frac{\pi z}{l}\right\} \tag{116}$$

where A is of order ϵ.

Substituting from equation (116) into the left-hand side of equation (115),

$$v_n = V_0 \cos \theta \left\{ 1 - \frac{R^2}{r^2} + A \frac{\pi}{l} K_1'\left(\frac{\pi r}{l}\right) \sin \frac{\pi z}{l} \right\} + O(\epsilon^2).$$

Substituting from equation (114),

$$v_n = V_0 \cos \theta \left\{ 1 - \left(1 + \epsilon \sin \frac{\pi z}{l}\right)^{-2} + A \frac{\pi}{l} K_1'\left(\frac{\pi R}{l}\right) \sin \frac{\pi z}{l} \right\}$$
$$+ O(\epsilon^2)$$
$$= V_0 \cos \theta \left\{ 2\epsilon \sin \frac{\pi z}{l} + A \frac{\pi}{l} K_1'\left(\frac{\pi R}{l}\right) \sin \frac{\pi z}{l} + O(\epsilon^2) \right\}.$$

Therefore $v_n = 0$ with error $O(\epsilon^2)$ if

$$A = \frac{-2\epsilon l}{\pi K_1'\left(\dfrac{\pi R}{l}\right)} = \frac{-2\epsilon l}{\pi K_0\left(\dfrac{\pi R}{l}\right) - \dfrac{l}{R} K_1\left(\dfrac{\pi R}{l}\right)}, \quad (117)$$

on using equation (95). The velocity potential is given, with error $O(\epsilon^2)$, by equations (116) and (117).

Exercise 10

Find the velocity potential if the axis of revolution of the solid of this section makes an angle $\dfrac{\pi}{2} - \alpha$ with the direction of the flow at infinity.

Answer

$\phi = \phi_1 \cos \alpha + \phi_2$, where ϕ_1 is given by equation (116) and ϕ_2
$= V_0 \sin \alpha \left[z + \epsilon R \cos \dfrac{\pi z}{l} K_0\left(\dfrac{\pi r}{l}\right) \left\{ K_0'\left(\dfrac{\pi R}{l}\right) \right\}^{-1} \right]$

4. AXI-SYMMETRICAL TEMPERATURE DISTRIBUTIONS IN A CYLINDER

If a variable expressed as a function of cylindrical polar co-ordinates, r, θ and z, is independent of θ, then that variable is said to be 'axially symmetric' or 'axi-symmetric'.

Case I. A right-circular metal cylinder is maintained at zero temperature on its curved surface $r = R$. The temperature distributions on its two plane ends are given and are functions of r only. The cylinder is of length $2l$. The problem is to determine the temperature distribution within the cylinder.

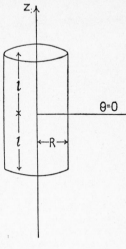

Fig. 12

The mathematical problem is to solve Laplace's equation subject to the conditions

$$T=0 \text{ on } r=R,$$
$$T=T_+(r), \text{ given, on } z=+l,$$

and

$$T=T_-(r), \text{ given, on } z=-l.$$

The problem is clearly axi-symmetric. In axial symmetry, the constant n in Bessel's equation is zero and the solution is expressed in terms either of zero order Bessel functions or of zero order modified Bessel functions. Since the temperature distributions on both ends can be expressed (see chapter 3, section 6) in series of zero order Bessel functions, we shall try a solution of which each term is of the form of equation (109), i.e. we try

$$T = \sum_{n=1}^{\infty} (A_n \, e^{+k_n z} + B_n \, e^{-k_n z}) \, J_0(k_n r). \tag{118}$$

In this problem $T=0$ at $r=R$; each term in equation (118) will satisfy this condition if

$$J_0(k_n R) = 0. \tag{119}$$

Equation (119) determines the values of k_n. The zeros of J_0 are given in many sets of tables.†

Equation (118) with equation (119) satisfies both Laplace's equation and the boundary condition on $r=R$. It remains to show that the A_n and B_n can be chosen to satisfy the conditions on the plane ends.

Using equations (97), (104) and (119), $T_+(r)$ and $T_-(r)$ can be expressed as

$$T_+(r) = \sum_{n=1}^{\infty} C_n \, J_0(k_n r) \tag{120}$$

where

$$C_n = \frac{2 \int_0^R T_+(r) \, r \, J_0(k_n r) \, dr}{R^2 \, J_1^2(k_n R)}, \tag{121}$$

and

$$T_-(r) = \sum_{n=1}^{\infty} D_n \, J_0(k_n r) \tag{122}$$

where

$$D_n = \frac{2 \int_0^R T_-(r) \, r \, J_0(k_n r) \, dr}{R^2 \, J_1^2(k_n R)}. \tag{123}$$

† If the boundary condition had been taken as $\frac{\partial T}{\partial r}$ at $r=R$, the equation to determine the k_n would have been $J'_0(k_n r) = 0$ at $r=R$ or $J_1(k_n R) = 0$. Since $J_1(0) = 0$, $k_1 = 0$ and equation (118) would need to be modified to

$$T = A_1 + B_1 z + \sum_{n=2}^{\infty} (A_n e^{+k_n z} + B_n e^{-k_n z}) J_0(k_n r).$$

Since $J_0(0) = 1$, all k_n are positive when the boundary condition is $T = 0$, at $r=R$.

E

Now $T_+(r)$ and $T_-(r)$ are the temperatures at $z= +l$ and $z= -l$ respectively. Therefore, from equation (118),

$$T_+(r)= \sum_{n=1}^{\infty} (A_n\, e^{k_n l} +B_n\, e^{-k_n l})\, J_0(k_n r) \qquad (124)$$

and

$$T_-(r)= \sum_{n=1}^{\infty} (A_n\, e^{-k_n l}+B_n\, e^{k_n l})\, J_0(k_n r). \qquad (125)$$

Equating coefficients of corresponding terms in the two equations for both $T_+(r)$ and $T_-(r)$,

$$C_n=A_n\, e^{k_n l}+B_n\, e^{-k_n l}$$

and

$$D_n=A_n\, e^{-k_n l}+B_n\, e^{k_n l}.$$

Solution of these equations gives the values of A_n and B_n, which must be chosen to satisfy the conditions on the plane ends, as

$$A_n=\frac{C_n\, e^{k_n l}-D_n\, e^{-k_n l}}{e^{2k_n l}-e^{-2k_n l}} \quad \text{and} \quad B_n=\frac{D_n\, e^{k_n l}-C_n\, e^{-k_n l}}{e^{2k_n l}-e^{-2k_n l}}.$$

Substituting back into equation (118),

$$T= \sum_{n=1}^{\infty} \frac{C_n \sinh k_n(l+z)+D_n \sinh k_n(l-z)}{\sinh 2k_n l}\, J_0(k_n r), \qquad (126)$$

where C_n and D_n are given by equations (121) and (123). In many cases that occur in practice, equations (121) and (123) will require numerical evaluation. In the example that follows an analytic evaluation is found.

Case II

As a particular case, suppose the end $z= +l$ is subject to a parabolic temperature distribution,

$$T_+(r)=T_0\left(1-\frac{r^2}{R^2}\right) \text{ where } T_0 \text{ is a constant,}$$

and the end $z= -l$ is at zero temperature, i.e.

$$T_-(r)=0.$$

From equation (123),

$$D_n = 0. \tag{127}$$

From equation (121),

$$C_n = \frac{2T_0 \int_0^R \left(1 - \frac{r^2}{R^2}\right) r \, J_0(k_n r) \, \mathrm{d}r}{R^2 \, J_1^2(k_n R)}. \tag{128}$$

From equation (84), $\dfrac{\mathrm{d}}{\mathrm{d}\rho}\big(\rho \, J_1(\rho)\big) = \rho \, J_0(\rho)$. Therefore, on integration by parts,

$$\int_0^R \left(1 - \frac{r^2}{R^2}\right) r \, J_0(k_n r) \, \mathrm{d}r$$

$$= \frac{1}{k_n}\left[\left(1 - \frac{r^2}{R^2}\right) r \, J_1(k_n r) \, \bigg|_0^R + \frac{2}{R^2} \int_0^R J_1(k_n r) \, \mathrm{d}r\right]$$

$$= \frac{2}{k_n R^2} \int_0^R r^2 \, J_1(k_n r) \, \mathrm{d}r.$$

Using equation (83) on integrating by parts again,

$$\int_0^R \left(1 - \frac{r^2}{R^2}\right) r \, J_0(k_n r) \, \mathrm{d}r$$

$$= -\frac{2}{k_n^2 R^2}\left[r^2 \, J_0(k_n r) \, \bigg|_0^R - 2 \int_0^R r \, J_0(k_n r) \, \mathrm{d}r\right]$$

$$= \frac{4}{k_n^2 R^2}\left[\frac{1}{k_n} r \, J_1(k_n r)\right]\bigg|_0^R$$

$$= \frac{4}{R k_n^3} \, J_1(k_n R).$$

Substituting back into equation (128),

$$C_n = \frac{8T_0}{R^3 k_n^3 J_1(k_n R)}. \tag{129}$$

Substitution from equations (127) and (129) into equation (126) gives the solution to this problem:

$$T = \frac{8T_0}{R^3} \sum_{n=1}^{\infty} \frac{\sinh k_n(l+z) \, J_0(k_n r)}{k_n^3 \sinh 2k_n l \, J_1(k_n R)}. \tag{130}$$

SOLUTIONS USING CYLINDRICAL POLAR CO-ORDINATES

Exercise 11

If the curved surface of the cylinder is thermally insulated (i.e. $\frac{\partial T}{\partial r} = 0$ at $r = R$) instead of being maintained at zero temperature, and the ends are maintained at $T_+(r)$ and $T_-(r)$ as before, show that the temperature distribution within the cylinder is given by

$$T = \frac{C_1 + D_1}{2} + \frac{C_1 - D_1}{2l}z + \sum_{n=2}^{\infty} C_n \frac{\sinh k_n(l+z) + D_n \sinh k_n(l-z)}{\sinh 2k_n l} J_0(k_n r),$$

where $C_1 = \frac{2}{R^2}\int_0^R T_+(r)r\,dr$, $D_1 = \frac{2}{R^2}\int_0^R T_-(r)r\,dr$ and, for $n \neq 1$,

$$C_n = \frac{2\int_0^R T_+(r)r\,J_0(k_n r)\,dr}{R^2 J_0(k_n R)} \quad \text{and} \quad D_n = \frac{2\int_0^R T_-(r)r\,J_0(k_n r)\,dr}{R^2 J_0^2(k_n R)}.$$

Exercise 12

The cylinder $0 \leqslant r \leqslant R$, $0 \leqslant z \leqslant l$, has its end faces maintained at temperature zero and its curved face $r = R$ maintained at $T = T_R(z)$. Show that the temperature distribution within the cylinder is given by

$$T = \sum_{n=1}^{\infty} A_n \frac{I_0(n\pi r/l)}{I_0(n\pi R/l)} \sin \frac{n\pi z}{l} \quad \text{where} \quad A_n = \frac{2}{l}\int_0^l T_R(z) \sin \frac{n\pi z}{l}\,dz.$$

Exercise 13

State an electrostatic problem for which the potential is given by equation (130).

Answer

A segment of space is bounded by a right circular cylinder with plane ends. The curved surface $r = R$ and the end $z = -l$ are at zero potential and the end $z = +l$ is at potential $T_0(1 - r^2/R^2)$. The potential inside the cylinder is given by equation (130).

CHAPTER FIVE

Legendre Polynomials

---

1. SOLUTION IN SERIES OF LEGENDRE'S EQUATION

In chapter 2, section 5, we found that Θ satisfied the equation

$$\left(n(n+1)\sin^2\theta - m^2\right)\Theta + \sin\theta\,\frac{\mathrm{d}}{\mathrm{d}\theta}\left(\sin\theta\,\frac{\mathrm{d}\Theta}{\mathrm{d}\theta}\right)=0, \quad (49)$$

where n > 0 and where m is positive integral or zero if ψ covers the entire range from 0 to 2π. If we put

$$\mu = \cos\theta \tag{131}$$

and $f(\theta)$ is any function of θ, then

$$\frac{\mathrm{d}f}{\mathrm{d}\theta} = \frac{\mathrm{d}f}{\mathrm{d}\mu}\cdot\frac{\mathrm{d}\mu}{\mathrm{d}\theta} = -\sin\theta\,\frac{\mathrm{d}f}{\mathrm{d}\mu}$$

and

$$\sin\theta\,\frac{\mathrm{d}f}{\mathrm{d}\theta} = -\sin^2\theta\,\frac{\mathrm{d}f}{\mathrm{d}\mu} = -(1-\mu^2)\,\frac{\mathrm{d}f}{\mathrm{d}\mu}.$$

Substituting in equation (49),

$$\left(n(n+1)(1-\mu^2)-m^2\right)\Theta + (1-\mu^2)\frac{\mathrm{d}}{\mathrm{d}\mu}\left((1-\mu^2)\frac{\mathrm{d}\Theta}{\mathrm{d}\mu}\right)=0$$

or

$$(1-\mu^2)\frac{\mathrm{d}^2\Theta}{\mathrm{d}\mu^2} - 2\mu\,\frac{\mathrm{d}\Theta}{\mathrm{d}\mu} + \left(n(n+1) - \frac{m^2}{1-\mu^2}\right)\Theta = 0. \tag{132}$$

Equation (132) is known as the *associated Legendre equation*. The particular case $m=0$ gives

$$(1-\mu^2)\frac{\mathrm{d}^2\Theta}{\mathrm{d}\mu^2} - 2\mu\frac{\mathrm{d}\Theta}{\mathrm{d}\mu} + n(n+1)\,\Theta = 0, \tag{133}$$

which is known as *Legendre's equation.* In this section attention will be confined to the solution of equation (133).

We shall look for a solution of equation (133) in the form of a power series in μ. The power series will be a solution of the equation over any range of μ in which it converges. We shall only consider solutions which converge over the entire physical range of μ. Since θ varies from 0 to π, the physical range of $\mu (= \cos \theta)$ is $1 \geqslant \mu \geqslant -1$.

Put

$$\Theta = \mu^\gamma \left(a_0 + a_1 \mu + \frac{a_2}{2!} \mu^2 + \ldots + \frac{a_r}{r!} \mu^r + \ldots \right), a_0 \neq 0, \quad (134)$$

then

$$\frac{d\Theta}{d\mu} = \gamma a_0 \mu^{\gamma-1} + (\gamma+1) a_1 \mu^\gamma + (\gamma+2) \frac{a_2}{2!} \mu^{\gamma+1} + \ldots$$
$$+ (\gamma+r) \frac{a_r}{r!} \mu^{\gamma+r-1} + \ldots$$

and

$$\frac{d^2\Theta}{d\mu^2} = \gamma(\gamma-1) a_0 \mu^{\gamma-2} + (\gamma+1)\gamma a_1 \mu^{\gamma-1} + (\gamma+2)(\gamma+1) \frac{a_2}{2!} \mu^\gamma$$
$$+ \ldots + (\gamma+r)(\gamma+r-1) \frac{a_r}{r!} \mu^{\gamma+r-2} + \ldots$$

On substituting back into equation (133), the lowest power of μ that occurs is $\mu^{\gamma-2}$. Its coefficient is $\gamma(\gamma-1)a_0$. Therefore the indicial equation gives

$$\gamma = 0 \quad \text{or} \quad \gamma = 1. \quad (135)$$

Equate to zero the other coefficients in ascending order:

$[\mu^{\gamma-1}]$ $\qquad\qquad (\gamma+1)\gamma a_1 = 0,$

whence, using equation (135),

either $\gamma = 0$ or $\gamma = 1$, $a_1 = 0$;

$[\mu^\gamma]$ $\quad (\gamma+2)(\gamma+1)\dfrac{a_2}{2!} - \gamma(\gamma-1)a_0 - 2\gamma a_0 + n(n+1)a_0 = 0,$

$$a_2 = 2! \frac{\gamma(\gamma+1) - n(n+1)}{(\gamma+2)(\gamma+1)} a_0;$$

$$[\mu^{\gamma+r-2}]\ (\gamma+r)(\gamma+r-1)\frac{a_r}{r!}-(\gamma+r-2)(\gamma+r-3)\frac{a_{r-2}}{(r-2)!}$$

$$-2(\gamma+r-2)\frac{a_{r-2}}{(r-2)!}+n(n+1)\frac{a_{r-2}}{(r-2)!}=0,$$

$$a_r=r(r-1)\frac{(\gamma+r-2)(\gamma+r-1)-n(n+1)}{(\gamma+r)(\gamma+r-1)}a_{r-2}.$$

If $\quad\gamma=0,\ a_r=\{(r-2)(r-1)-n(n+1)\}a_{r-2};\quad$ (136)

if $\quad\gamma=1,\ a_r=\dfrac{r-1}{r+1}\{(r-1)r-n(n+1)\}a_{r-2}.\quad$ (137)

It can be seen from equations (136) and (137) that both for $\gamma=0$ and for $\gamma=1$, the coefficients of even powers of μ will be independent of the coefficients of odd powers of μ and vice-versa. If $\gamma=0$ and $a_1\neq0$, the coefficients of odd powers of μ will depend only on a_1, the even powers only on a_0 and there will be in effect a sum of two independent series. But the series of odd powers has μ as a common factor and is identical with the series obtained for $\gamma=1$. Therefore we can take $a_1=0$ for both $\gamma=0$ and $\gamma=1$, and then, from equations (136) and (137), $a_r=0$ for all odd r in both cases.

Case I. $\gamma=0$.

The series will terminate at $a_{r-2}\mu^{r-2}$ if the coefficient of the right-hand side of equation (136) is zero. Solving $(r-2)(r-1)=n(n+1)$ for r, $r=n+2$ or $-n+1$. Since r is a positive even integer, the series will terminate at $a_n\mu^n$ when n is an even integer; by definition n is positive.

When n is not an even integer, the series does not terminate.

From equation (136),

$$a_r=(r-n-2)(r+n-1)a_{r-2}$$
$$=(r-n-2)(r-n-4)\ \ldots\ (r-n-r)$$
$$(r+n-1)(r+n-3)\ \ldots\ (r+n-(r-1))a_0.$$

Substituting in equation (134),

63

$$\Theta = a_0 \Big(1 +$$

$$\sum_{\substack{r=2 \\ r \text{ even}}}^{\infty} \frac{(r-n-2)(r-n-4)\ldots(-n)(r+n-1)(r+n-3)\ldots(n+1)\,\mu^r}{r!} \Big).$$

If we put $r = 2s$, the solution becomes

$$\Theta = a_0 \Big(1 +$$

$$\sum_{s=1}^{\infty} \frac{(2s-n-2)(2s-n-4)\ldots(-n)(2s+n-1)(2s+n-3)\ldots(n+1)\,\mu^{2s}}{(2s)!} \Big).$$

$$(138)$$

Let us now investigate whether this series converges for all μ in the range $-1 \leqslant \mu \leqslant 1$. The ratio of successive terms in the series is

$$\frac{v_{s+1}}{v_s} = \frac{(2s-n)(2s+n+1)}{(2s+1)(2s+2)} \mu^2,$$

where v_s denotes the s'th term of the series.

Expanding in powers of $\frac{1}{s}$,

$$\frac{v_{s+1}}{v_s} = \Big(1 - \frac{1}{s} + \mathrm{O}\Big(\frac{1}{s^2}\Big) \Big) \mu^2 \text{ as } s \to \infty. \qquad (139)$$

For $|\mu| < 1$, $\left| \dfrac{v_{s+1}}{v_s} \right| < 1$ as $s \to \infty$ and therefore the series is convergent by the ratio test.† For $\mu = 1$, $\dfrac{v_{s+1}}{v_s} \to 1$ as $s \to \infty$ and the ratio test is indeterminate in this case.

We shall show that the series is divergent for $\mu = \pm 1$ by comparison with the series $1 + \sum_{s=2}^{\infty} (s \ln s)^{-1}$. Now

$$1 + \sum_{s=2}^{N} (s \ln s)^{-1} > 1 + \int_{2}^{N+1} (s \ln s)^{-1} \mathrm{d}s = 1 + \ln(\ln s) \Big|_{2}^{N+1}.$$

† See, e.g., J. A. Green, *Sequences and Series*, uniform with this volume.

But $\ln(\ln s) \to \infty$ as $s \to \infty$ and therefore $1 + \sum\limits_{s=2}^{\infty} (s \ln s)^{-1}$ is divergent. The ratio of successive terms in this series is, denoting the s'th term by u_s,

$$\frac{u_{s+1}}{u_s} = \frac{s \ln s}{\left(s+1\right) \ln(s+1)} = \frac{\ln s}{\left(1+\frac{1}{s}\right)\left(\ln s + \ln\left(1+\frac{1}{s}\right)\right)}$$

$$= \left(1+\frac{1}{s}\right)^{-1}\left(1+\left\{\frac{1}{s}+O\left(\frac{1}{s^2}\right)\right\}\left(\ln s\right)^{-1}\right)^{-1}$$

$$= 1 - \frac{1}{s} - \frac{1}{s \ln s} + O\left(\frac{1}{s^2}\right).$$

Comparison with equation (139) shows that

$$\frac{v_{s+1}}{v_s} > \frac{u_{s+1}}{u_s} > 0 \quad \text{as } s \to \infty \text{ for } \mu = \pm 1.$$

Therefore the series $\sum\limits_{s=1}^{\infty} v_s$ is divergent for $\mu = \pm 1$, because the series $\sum\limits_{s=1}^{\infty} u_s$ is divergent; i.e. the right-hand side of equation (138) is divergent for $\mu = \pm 1$.

In physical problems in which we want a solution for $0 \leqslant \theta \leqslant \pi$ or $1 \geqslant \mu \geqslant -1$, the power series solution for $\gamma = 0$ will only be valid for the whole range of μ when n is an even integer, and in this case the series terminates.

Case II. $\gamma = 1$.

The series will terminate at $a_{r-2}\mu^{r-1}$ if the right-hand side of equation (137) is zero. Solving $(r-1)r = n(n+1)$ for r, we find that $r = n+1$ or $-n$. Since r is a positive even integer, the series will terminate at $a_{n-1}\mu^n$ only when n is an odd integer.

When n is not an odd integer, the series does not terminate. The ratio R of successive terms in the infinite series is, from equation (134),

$$R = \frac{1}{(r-1)r} \frac{a_r}{a_{r-2}} \mu^2.$$

Substituting from equation (137) and putting $r = 2s$,

$$R = \frac{(2s-1)2s - n(n+1)}{2s(2s+1)} \mu^2$$

$$= \left(1 - \frac{1}{s} + O\left(\frac{1}{s^2}\right)\right) \mu^2 \text{ as } s \to \infty.$$

By a treatment identical to that of equation (139), it can be shown that the series converges for $-1 < \mu < 1$ but diverges at $\mu = \pm 1$. Therefore the power series solution for $\gamma = 1$ will only be valid for the whole physical range of μ, $-1 \leqslant \mu \leqslant 1$, if n is an odd integer.

To sum up, the solution by series gives two solutions of Legendre's equation. However, only when n is an integer, is either of the solutions convergent for all μ, $-1 \leqslant \mu \leqslant 1$. When n is an even integer, it is the solution whose leading term is a constant; when n is an odd integer, it is the solution whose leading term is a constant times μ. In these cases the series terminate and the solutions are known as *Legendre polynomials*, apart from arbitrary multiplicative constants. In all other cases the solutions are infinite series, convergent for $-1 < \mu < 1$ but divergent for $\mu = \pm 1$. These solutions are called *Legendre functions* and will not be considered further in this book. Note that the values of μ for divergence, $\mu = \pm 1$, are the values of μ for which the coefficient of the highest order term in the differential equation (133) is zero. Explicit expressions for the Legendre polynomials will now be found.

For n even, $\gamma = 0$, all suffixes r are even, and by equation (138)

$$\begin{aligned}
a_r &= -(n+r-1)(n-r+2)a_{r-2} \\
&= (-)^2(n+r-1)(n+r-3)(n-r+2)(n-r+4)a_{r-4} \\
&= (-)^{r/2}[(n+r-1)(n+r-3) \ldots (n+1)] \\
&\qquad [(n-r+2)(n-r+4) \ldots n] \, a_0.
\end{aligned}$$

To express the products in square brackets in terms of factorial functions, the product of odd numbers is completed by putting in the missing even numbers and each term in the product of even numbers is divided by two to produce a product of successive numbers.

i.e.

$$a_r = (-)^{r/2} \left[\frac{(n+r)(n+r-1)(n+r-2) \ldots (n+1)}{2^{r/2}\left(\frac{n}{2}+\frac{r}{2}\right)\left(\frac{n}{2}+\frac{r}{2}-1\right) \ldots \left(\frac{n}{2}+1\right)} \right]$$

$$\left[2^{r/2}\left(\frac{n}{2}-\frac{r}{2}+1\right)\left(\frac{n}{2}-\frac{r}{2}+2\right) \ldots \frac{n}{2} \right] a_0$$

$$= (-)^{r/2} \frac{(n+r)!\left(\frac{n}{2}!\right)^2}{\left(\frac{n}{2}+\frac{r}{2}\right)! \, n! \, \left(\frac{n}{2}-\frac{r}{2}\right)!} a .$$

Substituting back into equation (134) and remembering that the series terminates at $a_n \mu^n / n!$,

$$\Theta = \frac{\left(\frac{n}{2}!\right)^2 a_0}{n!} \sum_{\substack{r=0 \\ r \text{ even}}}^{n} \frac{(-)^{r/2}(n+r)!}{\left(\frac{n}{2}+\frac{r}{2}\right)!\left(\frac{n}{2}-\frac{r}{2}\right)! \, r!} \mu^r.$$

Put $n-r=2s$, then

$$\Theta = (-)^{n/2} \frac{\left(\frac{n}{2}!\right)^2 a_0}{n!} \sum_{s=0}^{n/2} \frac{(-)^s (2n-2s)!}{(n-s)! \, s! \, (n-2s)!} \mu^{n-2s}.$$

$$(140)$$

For n odd, $\gamma = 1$, all suffices r are even, and by equation (139)

$$a_r = -\frac{r-1}{r+1}(n+r)(n-r+1)a_{r-2}$$

$$= (-)^2 \frac{r-3}{r+1}(n+r)(n+r-2)(n-r+1)(n-r+3)a_{r-4}$$

$$= (-)^{r/2} \frac{1}{r+1}[(n+r)(n+r-2) \ldots (n+2)]$$

$$[(n-r+1)(n-r+3) \ldots (n-1)]a_0$$

$$=(-)^{r/2}\frac{1}{r+1}\left[\frac{(n+r+1)(n+r)(n+r-1)\ldots(n+2)}{2^{r/2}\left(\frac{n}{2}+\frac{r}{2}+\frac{1}{2}\right)\left(\frac{n}{2}+\frac{r}{2}-\frac{1}{2}\right)\ldots\left(\frac{n}{2}+\frac{3}{2}\right)}\right]$$

$$\left[2^{r/2}\left(\frac{n}{2}-\frac{r}{2}+\frac{1}{2}\right)\left(\frac{n}{2}-\frac{r}{2}+\frac{3}{2}\right)\ldots\left(\frac{n}{2}-\frac{1}{2}\right)\right]a_0$$

$$=(-)^{r/2}\frac{1}{r+1}\frac{(n+r+1)!\,\frac{n+1}{2}!\,\frac{n-1}{2}!}{\frac{n+r+1}{2}!\,(n+1)!\,\frac{n-r-1}{2}!}\,a_0.$$

Substituting back into equation (134) and remembering that the series terminates at $a_{n-1}\mu^n/(n-1)!$,

$$\Theta=\frac{\frac{n+1}{2}!\,\frac{n-1}{2}!\,a_0}{(n+1)!}\sum_{\substack{r=0\\r\text{ even}}}^{n-1}\frac{(-)^{r/2}(n+r+1)!}{\frac{n+r+1}{2}!\,\frac{n-r-1}{2}!\,(r+1)!}\,\mu^{r+1}.$$

Put $n-r-1=2s$, then

$$\Theta=(-)^{(n-1)/2}\,\frac{\frac{n+1}{2}!\,\frac{n-1}{2}!\,a_0}{(n-1)!}\sum_{s=0}^{(n-1)/2}\frac{(-)^s(2n-2s)!}{(n-s)!\,s!\,(n-2s)!}\,\mu^{n-2s}.$$

$$\tag{141}$$

If we define $P_n(\mu)$ by

$$P_n(\mu)=\frac{1}{2^n}\sum_{s=0}^{\nu}\frac{(-)^s\,(2n-2s)!}{(n-s)!\,s!\,(n-2s)!}\,\mu^{n-2s},\tag{142}$$

where

$$\nu=\begin{cases}\frac{1}{2}n\text{ if }n\text{ is even}\\\frac{1}{2}(n-1)\text{ if }n\text{ is odd},\end{cases}\tag{143}$$

then, by equations (140) and (141), $P_n(\mu)$ is a solution of Legendre's equation for positive integral n. $P_n(\mu)$ differs from Θ in equations (140) and (141) only by arbitrary multiplicative constants. The constant in equation (142) is chosen so that $P_n(1)=1$ (proved later). Of course $A_nP_n(\mu)$

satisfies Legendre's equation where A_n is any constant. $P_n(\mu)$ is called the *Legendre polynomial of degree n*. Note that the highest power occurring in $P_n(\mu)$ is μ^n.

A compact formula for Legendre polynomials has been given by *Rodrigue*. It is

$$P_n(\mu) = \frac{1}{2^n.\,n!} \frac{d^n}{d\mu^n} (\mu^2 - 1)^n. \tag{144}$$

This result is proved by expanding $(\mu^2 - 1)^n$ by the binomial theorem and then differentiating:

$$\frac{1}{2^n.\,n!} \frac{d^n}{d\mu^n}(\mu^2-1)^n = \frac{1}{2^n.\,n!} \frac{d^n}{d\mu^n}\left\{\sum_{r=0}^{n}(-)^r \frac{n!}{r!\,(n-r)!}\mu^{2n-2r}\right\}$$

$$= \frac{1}{2^n} \sum_{r=0}^{\nu} (-)^r \frac{(2n-2r)!}{r!\,(n-r)!\,(n-2r)!}\,\mu^{n-2r}.$$

The sum ends at the term for which $n-2\nu=0$ or 1, i.e. $\nu=\dfrac{n}{2}$ if n is even, $\nu=\dfrac{n-1}{2}$ if n is odd. Hence by equations (142) and (143), the right-hand side of equation (144) is equal to $P_n(\mu)$. The compact nature of Rodrigue's formula makes it very suitable for use when algebraic manipulations of Legendre polynomials are performed (e.g. in section 3).

2. ASSOCIATED LEGENDRE FUNCTIONS

We shall now find some solutions of the associated Legendre equation (132).

Differentiate equation (133) m times with respect to μ:

$$(1-\mu^2)\frac{d^{m+2}\Theta}{d\mu^{m+2}} - 2\mu m\,\frac{d^{m+1}\Theta}{d\mu^{m+1}} - m(m-1)\frac{d^m\Theta}{d\mu^m} - 2\mu\frac{d^{m+1}\Theta}{d\mu^{m+1}}$$

$$-2m\frac{d^m\Theta}{d\mu^m} + n(n+1)\frac{d^m\Theta}{d\mu^m} = 0.$$

Put

$$T = \frac{\mathrm{d}^m \Theta}{\mathrm{d}\mu^m}, \tag{145}$$

then

$$(1-\mu^2)\frac{\mathrm{d}^2 T}{\mathrm{d}\mu^2} - 2(m+1)\mu\frac{dT}{d\mu} + \Big(n(n+1) - m(m+1)\Big)T = 0. \tag{146}$$

Put

$$\chi = (1-\mu^2)^{m/2}T, \tag{147}$$

then

$$\frac{\mathrm{d}T}{\mathrm{d}\mu} = (1-\mu^2)^{-m/2}\frac{\mathrm{d}\chi}{\mathrm{d}\mu} + m\mu(1-\mu^2)^{-m/2-1}\chi$$

and

$$\frac{\mathrm{d}^2 T}{\mathrm{d}\mu^2} = (1-\mu^2)^{-m/2}\frac{\mathrm{d}^2 \chi}{\mathrm{d}\mu^2} + 2m\mu(1-\mu^2)^{-m/2-1}\frac{\mathrm{d}\chi}{\mathrm{d}\mu}$$
$$+ \Big(m(m+2)\ \mu^2\ (1-\mu^2)^{-m/2-2} + m(1-\mu^2)^{-m/2-1}\Big)\chi.$$

Substituting in equation (146),

$$(1-\mu^2)\frac{\mathrm{d}^2 \chi}{\mathrm{d}\mu^2} - 2\mu\frac{\mathrm{d}\chi}{\mathrm{d}\mu} + \Big(n(n+1) - \frac{m^2}{1-\mu^2}\Big)\chi = 0. \tag{132}$$

But this equation is none other than the associated Legendre equation (132). Since $P_n(\mu)$ is a solution of equation (133), a solution of equation (132), denoted by $P_n^m(\mu)$, is given by

$$P_n^m(\mu) = (1-\mu^2)^{m/2}T = (1-\mu^2)^{m/2}\frac{\mathrm{d}^m P_n(\mu)}{\mathrm{d}\mu^m}, \tag{148}$$

where equations (147) and (145) have been used. The $P_n^m(\mu)$ are known as *associated Legendre functions*. Note that $P_n^o(\mu) = P_n(\mu)$.

If we substitute for $P_n(\mu)$ from Rodrigue's formula, equation (144),

$$P_n^m(\mu) = \frac{1}{2^n.\ n!}(1-\mu^2)^{m/2}\frac{\mathrm{d}^{m+n}(\mu^2-1)^n}{\mathrm{d}\mu^{m+n}}. \tag{149}$$

Since the highest order power in $P_n(\mu)$ is μ^n,

$$P_n^m(\mu) = 0 \text{ if } m > n. \tag{150}$$

Also

$$P_n^m(-\mu) = \frac{1}{2^n \cdot n!}(1-\mu^2)^{m/2}\frac{d^{m+n}(\mu^2-1)^n}{(-)^{m+n}d^{m+n}\mu} = (-)^{m+n} P_n^m(\mu).$$
(151)

and

$$P_n^n(\mu) = \frac{(2n)!}{2^n \cdot n!}(1-\mu^2)^{n/2}.$$
(152)

The Legendre polynomials and associated Legendre functions for $n=0$, 1, 2 and 3 are

$$\left.\begin{aligned}
P_0(\mu) &= 1 \\
P_1(\mu) &= \mu = \cos\theta \\
P_1^1(\mu) &= (1-\mu^2)^{1/2} = \sin\theta \\
P_2(\mu) &= \tfrac{1}{2}(3\mu^2-1) = \tfrac{1}{4}(3\cos 2\theta+1) \\
P_2^1(\mu) &= 3(1-\mu^2)^{1/2}\mu = \tfrac{3}{2}\sin 2\theta \\
P_2^2(\mu) &= 3(1-\mu^2) = \tfrac{3}{2}(1-\cos 2\theta) \\
P_3(\mu) &= \tfrac{1}{2}(5\mu^3-3\mu) = \tfrac{1}{8}(5\cos 3\theta+3\cos\theta) \\
P_3^1(\mu) &= \tfrac{3}{2}(1-\mu^2)^{1/2}(5\mu^2-1) = \tfrac{3}{8}(\sin\theta+5\sin 3\theta) \\
P_3^2(\mu) &= 15(1-\mu^2)\mu = \tfrac{15}{4}(\cos\theta-\cos 3\theta) \\
P_3^3(\mu) &= 15(1-\mu^2)^{3/2} = \tfrac{15}{4}(3\sin\theta-\sin 3\theta).
\end{aligned}\right\}$$
(153)

3. DERIVATIVE AND RECURRENCE FORMULAE FOR LEGENDRE POLYNOMIALS

Formula I:
$$(1-\mu^2)\,P_n'(\mu) = (n+1)(\mu P_n(\mu) - P_{n+1}(\mu)).$$
(154)
Proof:

$$P_{n+1}(\mu)$$

$$= \frac{1}{2^{n+1}(n+1)!}\frac{d^{n+1}}{d\mu^{n+1}}(\mu^2-1)^{n+1}$$

$$= \frac{1}{2^{n+1}(n+1)!}\frac{d^{n+1}}{d\mu^{n+1}}\left\{(\mu^2-1)(\mu^2-1)^n\right\}$$

$$= \frac{\mu^2-1}{2^{n+1}(n+1)!}\frac{d^{n+1}}{d\mu^{n+1}}(\mu^2-1)^n + \frac{\mu}{2^n n!}\frac{d^n}{d\mu^n}(\mu^2-1)^n$$

$$+ \frac{1}{2^{n+1}(n-1)!}\frac{d^{n-1}}{d\mu^{n-1}}(\mu^2-1)^n;$$
(155)

also

$$P_{n+1}(\mu)$$

$$=\frac{1}{2^{n+1}(n+1)!}\frac{d^n}{d\mu^n}\left\{\frac{d}{d\mu}(\mu^2-1)^{n+1}\right\}=\frac{1}{2^n.n!}\frac{d^n}{d\mu^n}\left\{\mu(\mu^2-1)^n\right\}$$

$$=\frac{1}{2^n.(n-1)!}\frac{d^{n-1}}{d\mu^{n-1}}(\mu^2-1)^n+\frac{\mu}{2^n.n!}\frac{d^n}{d\mu^n}(\mu^2-1)^n. \quad (156)$$

Subtract equation (156) from twice equation (155) to eliminate $\frac{d^{n-1}}{d\mu^{n-1}}(\mu^2-1)^n$:

$$P_{n+1}(\mu)=\frac{\mu^2-1}{2^n.(n+1)!}\frac{d^{n+1}}{d\mu^{n+1}}(\mu^2-1)^n+\frac{\mu}{2^n.n!}\frac{d^n}{d\mu^n}(\mu^2-1)^n$$

$$=-\frac{1-\mu^2}{n+1}P_n{}'(\mu)+\mu P_n(\mu).$$

Multiply through by $n+1$ to give equation (154).

Formula II:

$$(n+2)P_{n+1}(\mu)-(2n+3)\mu P_{n+1}(\mu)+(n+1)P_n(\mu)=0. \quad (157)$$

Proof: Differentiate equation (154) with respect to μ,

$$\frac{d}{d\mu}(1-\mu^2)P_n{}'(\mu)=(n+1)\{P_n(\mu)+\mu P_n{}'(\mu)-P_n{}'_{+1}(\mu)\}.$$

Substitute on the left-hand side from Legendre's equation (133) and for the derivatives on the right-hand side from equation (154):

$$-n(n+1)P_n(\mu)=(n+1)P_n(\mu)$$

$$+\frac{n+1}{1-\mu^2}\{(n+1)\mu(\mu P_n(\mu)-P_{n+1}(\mu))-(n+2)(\mu P_{n+1}(\mu)$$

$$-P_{n+2}(\mu))\}.$$

Simplification gives equation (157).

Formula III:

$$(1-\mu^2)P_n{}'(\mu)=n(P_{n-1}(\mu)-\mu P_n(\mu)). \quad (158)$$

This is proved by replacing n by $n-1$ in equation (157) and then using the equation so found to eliminate $P_{n+1}(\mu)$ from equation (154).

From equation (157), it will be shown that

$$P_n(1)=1. \qquad (159)$$

The proof is by induction. Suppose the result true for $r \leqslant n+1$. Then from equation (157),

$$(n+2)\,P_{n+2}(1)=(2n+3)\,P_{n+1}(1)-(n+1)\,P_n(1)=n+2.$$

Therefore the result is true for $r=n+2$ if it is true for $r \leqslant n+1$. But $P_0(1)=P_1(1)=1$ and therefore by induction the result is true for all n.

By equations (151) and (159),

$$P_n(-1)=(-)^n\,P_n(1)=(-)^n. \qquad (160)$$

Formula IV:

$$P'_{n+1}(\mu)-P'_{n-1}(\mu)=(2n+1)\,P_n(\mu). \qquad (161)$$

From equation (158) with n replaced by $n+1$ and equation (154) with n replaced by $n-1$,

$$(1-\mu^2)\,P'_{n+1}(\mu)-(1-\mu^2)\,P'_{n-1}(\mu)$$
$$=(n+1)\,P_n(\mu)-(n+1)\mu P_{n+1}(\mu)-n\mu P_{n-1}(\mu)+nP_n(\mu).$$

By equation (157) with n replaced by $n-1$,

$$(n+1)\,P_{n+1}(\mu)-(2n+1)\mu P_n(\mu)+nP_{n-1}(\mu)=0.$$

$$\therefore \quad (1-\mu^2)\{P'_{n+1}(\mu)-P'_{n-1}(\mu)\}=(2n+1)P_n(\mu)$$
$$-\mu^2(2n+1)P_n(\mu)$$

and equation (161) follows on dividing through by $1-\mu^2$.

Exercise 14

Prove the formula due to Hargreaves:

$$\frac{d}{d\mu}\{\mu(\,(P_n)^2+(P_{n+1})^2)-2P_nP_{n+1}\}=(2n+3)(P_{n+1})^2-(2n+1)(P_n)^2.$$

Hint: Use equation (154) for P_n' and equation (158) with $n+1$ instead of n for P'_{n+1}.

Exercise 15

By the same arguments used in deriving equations (154) and (157) only more complicated in detail, show that

$$(1-\mu^2)P_n^{m\prime}(\mu)=(n+1)\mu P_n^m(\mu)-(n+1-m)P_{n+1}^m(\mu) \qquad (162)$$

and

$$(n+2-m)\,P_{n+2}^m(\mu)-(2n+3)\mu P_{n+1}^m(\mu)+(n+1+m)\,P_n^m(\mu)=0. \qquad (163)$$

4. SERIES OF LEGENDRE POLYNOMIALS

In this section we assume a function $f(\mu)$ can be expanded, in the interval $-1 \leqslant \mu \leqslant 1$, as an infinite sum of Legendre polynomials of the form

$$f(\mu) = \sum_{n=0}^{\infty} A_n P_n(\mu). \tag{164}$$

We shall determine the coefficients A_n.

If equation (164) is multiplied by $P_m(\mu)$ and then integrated with respect to μ from -1 to $+1$, terms of the form

$$\int_{-1}^{1} P_n(\mu) P_m(\mu) \, \mathrm{d}\mu$$

and

$$\int_{-1}^{1} \Big(P_n(\mu) \Big)^2 \, \mathrm{d}\mu$$

appear on the right-hand side. These integrals are now evaluated.

Since $P_n(\mu)$ satisfies Legendre's equation

$$\frac{\mathrm{d}}{\mathrm{d}\mu} \Big\{ (1-\mu^2) \frac{\mathrm{d} P_n(\mu)}{\mathrm{d}\mu} \Big\} + n(n+1) P_n(\mu) = 0.$$

Multiply through by $P_m(\mu)$ and integrate with respect to μ from -1 to $+1$,

$$\int_{-1}^{1} P_m(\mu) \frac{\mathrm{d}}{\mathrm{d}\mu} \Big\{ (1-\mu^2) \frac{\mathrm{d} P_n(\mu)}{\mathrm{d}\mu} \Big\} \mathrm{d}\mu$$

$$+ n(n+1) \int_{-1}^{1} P_m(\mu) P_n(\mu) \, \mathrm{d}\mu = 0.$$

Integrate the first term by parts. Since $1-\mu^2$ vanishes at $\mu = \pm 1$,

$$- \int_{-1}^{1} (1-\mu^2) \frac{\mathrm{d} P_n(\mu)}{\mathrm{d}\mu} \frac{\mathrm{d} P_m(\mu)}{\mathrm{d}\mu} \, \mathrm{d}\mu$$

$$+ n(n+1) \int_{-1}^{1} P_m(\mu) P_n(\mu) \, \mathrm{d}\mu = 0.$$

If we had started with the equation satisfied by $P_m(\mu)$ and multiplied by $P_n(\mu)$, the result would have been the same except that m and n would be interchanged; i.e.

74

$$-\int_{-1}^{1}(1-\mu^2)\,\frac{\mathrm{d}\,P_m(\mu)}{\mathrm{d}\mu}\,\frac{\mathrm{d}\,P_n(\mu)}{\mathrm{d}\mu}\,\mathrm{d}\mu$$

$$+m(m+1)\int_{-1}^{1}P_n(\mu)\,P_m(\mu)\,\mathrm{d}\mu=0.$$

Subtracting the last two equations,

$$\{n(n+1)-m(m+1)\}\int_{-1}^{1}P_n(\mu)\,P_m(\mu)\,\mathrm{d}\mu=0.$$

The factor before the integral equals $(n-m)(n+m+1)$. Therefore, if $n \neq m$,

$$\int_{-1}^{1}P_n(\mu)\,P_m(\mu)\,\mathrm{d}\mu=0. \tag{165}$$

In the particular case of $m=0$, $P_m(\mu)=1$ and

$$\int_{-1}^{1}P_n(\mu)\,\mathrm{d}\mu=0 \text{ if } n \neq 0. \tag{166}$$

Since the highest power of μ with a non-zero coefficient occurring in $P_n(\mu)$ is μ^n, any polynomial of degree n in μ, $Q_n(\mu)$ say, can be expressed as

$$Q_n(\mu)=\sum_{r=0}^{n}A_r\,P_r(\mu),$$

where the A_r are constants. Therefore

$$\int_{-1}^{1}P_m(\mu)\,Q_n(\mu)\,\mathrm{d}\mu=\sum_{r=0}^{n}A_r\int_{-1}^{1}P_m(\mu)\,P_r(\mu)\,\mathrm{d}\mu$$

$$=0 \text{ if } n<m, \tag{167}$$

by equation (165).

To evaluate $\int_{-1}^{1}\Big(P_n(\mu)\Big)^2\mathrm{d}\mu$, multiply through equation (161) by $P_n(\mu)$ and integrate from -1 to 1. This gives

$$(2n+1)\int_{-1}^{1}\Big(P_n(\mu)\Big)^2\mathrm{d}\mu$$

$$=\int_{-1}^{1}P'_{n+1}(\mu)\,P_n(\mu)\,\mathrm{d}\mu-\int_{-1}^{1}P'_{n-1}(\mu)\,P_n(\mu)\,\mathrm{d}\mu.$$

But $P'_{n-1}(\mu)$ is a polynomial of degree $n-2$ in μ and therefore the last integral is zero. On integration by parts of the first integral on the right-hand side,

$$(2n+1) \int_{-1}^{1} \Big(P_n(\mu)\Big)^2 \, d\mu$$

$$= P_{n+1}(\mu) \, P_n(\mu) \, \Big|_{-1}^{1} - \int_{-1}^{1} P_{n+1}(\mu) \, P_n'(\mu) \, du.$$

The last integral is again zero. Using equations (159) and (160),

$$(2n+1) \int_{-1}^{1} \Big(P_n(\mu)\Big)^2 \, d\mu = 1 - (-)^{n+1}(-)^n = 2.$$

Therefore

$$\int_{-1}^{1} \Big(P_n(\mu)\Big)^2 \, d\mu = \frac{2}{2n+1} \, . \tag{168}$$

Now multiply equation (164) by $P_m(\mu)$ and integrate with respect to μ from -1 to 1:

$$\int_{-1}^{1} f(\mu) \, P_m(\mu) \, d\mu = \sum_{n=0}^{\infty} A_n \int_{-1}^{1} P_n(\mu) \, P_m(\mu) \, d\mu$$

$$= \frac{2}{2m+1} \, A_m,$$

since all integrals on the right-hand side for which $n \neq m$ vanish and that for $n=m$ is equal to $\frac{2}{2m+1}$. Therefore

$$A_m = (m + \tfrac{1}{2}) \int_{-1}^{1} f(\mu) \, P_m(\mu) \, d\mu. \tag{169}$$

We have now determined the coefficients in the series for $f(\mu)$, equation (164).

Exercise 16

Show that $\int_{-1}^{1} P_n^m(\mu) \, P_l^m(\mu) \, d\mu = 0$ if $n \neq l$.

Hint: Use the same method as in the last section but with the associated Legendre equation.

(It can be shown that $\int_{-1}^{1} (P_n^m(\mu))^2 \, d\mu = \frac{2}{2n+1} \frac{(n+m)!}{(n-m)!}$ and hence unctions can be expanded as series of associated Legendre functions in the interval $-1 \leqslant \mu \leqslant 1$.)

Exercise 17

Show that $(1 - 2\mu h + h^2)^{-\frac{1}{2}}$ can be expanded as $\sum_{n=0}^{\infty} P_n(\mu) h^n$ provided h is sufficiently small for the series to be convergent. Because of this property $(1 - 2\mu h + h^2)^{-\frac{1}{2}}$ is called the 'generating function' for Legendre polynomials.

CHAPTER SIX

Solutions Using Spherical Polar Co-ordinates

1. FORM OF SOLUTIONS OF LAPLACE'S EQUATION

In chapter 2, section 5, we looked for solutions of Laplace's equation in spherical polar co-ordinates, r, θ, ψ of the form

$$\phi = R(r)\,\Theta(\theta)\,\Psi(\psi). \tag{46}$$

Equations (51) and (52) give $R(r)$ and $\Psi(\psi)$ for $m > 0$. For solutions to be valid over the usual physical range of θ and ψ, i.e. $0 \leqslant \theta \leqslant \pi$ and $0 \leqslant \psi \leqslant 2\pi$, m and n must be positive integral or zero. In these circumstances $\Theta(\theta) = P_n^m(\mu)$ where $\mu = \cos\theta$. Substituting back into equation (46), the solutions are of the form

$$\phi = \binom{r^n}{r^{-n-1}} P_n^m(\cos\theta) \binom{\sin}{\cos} m\psi. \tag{170}$$

If, in a particular problem, ϕ must be finite at $r = 0$, solutions containing r^{-n-1} are excluded, if ϕ must remain finite as $r \to \infty$, solutions containing r^n ($n > 0$) are excluded.

2. SPHERE MOVING IN A LIQUID AT REST AT INFINITY

A sphere of radius a moves with velocity U in an irrota-

Fig. 13

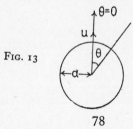

78

tional incompressible liquid. Find the velocity field in the liquid given that it is at rest at infinity. The component of liquid velocity normal to the surface of the sphere must equal the component of U along the normal because no liquid crosses the surface; i.e.

$$v_r = \frac{\partial \phi}{\partial r} = U \cos \theta \text{ at } r = a.$$

There are two terms in equation (170) whose θ-dependence is of the form $\cos \theta$ and which are independent of ψ, namely $r \cos \theta$ and $r^{-2} \cos \theta$. But the former is not finite as $r \to \infty$, therefore we try

$$\phi = Ar^{-2} \cos \theta.$$

To satisfy the boundary condition on $r = a$,

$$-2Aa^{-3} = U \text{ or } A = -\tfrac{1}{2}Ua^3;$$

whence

$$\phi = -\tfrac{1}{2}Ua^3r^{-2} \cos \theta.$$

The velocity components are

$$v_r = \frac{\partial \phi}{\partial r} = Ua^3r^{-3} \cos \theta,$$

$$v_\theta = \frac{1}{r} \frac{\partial \phi}{\partial \theta} = \tfrac{1}{2}Ua^3r^{-3} \sin \theta$$

and

$$v_\psi = \frac{1}{r \sin \theta} \frac{\partial \phi}{\partial \psi} = 0.$$

3. A CHARGED CONDUCTING SPHERE IN A UNIFORM ELECTRIC FIELD

Let the radius of the sphere be a and let $\theta = 0$ lie in the direction of the undisturbed electric field, which has strength E_0. Let the charge on the sphere be Q. The problem is symmetric about the axis $\theta = 0$ and the co-ordinate ψ will not appear in the solution.

Since the effect of the sphere will be negligible at a

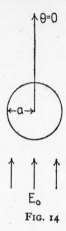

FIG. 14

large distance, the field will tend to E_0 at infinity, i.e. the potential will satisfy

$$V \sim -E_0 z + A = -E_0 r \cos \theta + A \text{ as } r \to \infty, \qquad (171)$$

where A is a constant. The notation $V \sim f(r)$ as $r \to R$ is used to mean $V = f(r) + g(r)$, where $g(r)/f(r) \to 0$ as $r \to R$.

Since the surface of the sphere is conducting, the potential is constant over its surface, i.e.

$$V = \text{const. on } r = a. \qquad (172)$$

V must now be found to satisfy Laplace's equation subject to the boundary conditions, equations (171) and (172). Since $\cos \theta$ and constants appear in the boundary conditions which are for constant r, let us pick out the terms in equation (170) which contain $\cos \theta$ and those that are independent of θ. Remembering $P_1(\cos \theta) = \cos \theta$, we try

$$V = Cr \cos \theta + Dr^{-2} \cos \theta + F + Gr^{-1}.$$

To satisfy equation (171), $C = -E_0$, $F = A$, whence

$$V = -E_0 r \cos \theta + Dr^{-2} \cos \theta + A + Gr^{-1}.$$

To satisfy equation (172),

$$-E_0 a + Da^{-2} = 0, \quad D = E_0 a^3,$$

whence

$$V = -E_0 \cos \theta (r - a^3 r^{-2}) + A + G r^{-1}. \qquad (173)$$

Now ρ, the surface charge per unit area, is given by

$$4\pi\rho = E_n = -\left(\frac{\partial V}{\partial r}\right)_{r=a}.$$

Substituting from equation (173),

$$\rho = \frac{3E_0 \cos \theta}{4\pi} + \frac{G}{4\pi a^2}.$$

The total charge on the sphere

$$= Q = \int_S \rho \, dS = 2\pi a^2 \int_0^\pi \sin \theta \left(\frac{3E_0 \cos \theta}{4\pi} + \frac{G}{4\pi a^2}\right) d\theta = G.$$

Therefore

$$V = -E_0 \cos \theta (r - a^3 r^{-2}) + A + Q r^{-1} \qquad (174)$$

is the potential outside and on the sphere. The constant A is arbitrary and does not affect the electric field.

4. DIELECTRIC SPHERE IN A UNIFORM ELECTRIC FIELD

This problem is of particular interest because it involves matching two solutions of Laplace's equation. The electrostatic potential V satisfies Laplace's equation both inside and outside the sphere and is continuous across the boundary. If K denotes the dielectric constant, then K times the normal component of the electric field is also continuous across the boundary.

Let the sphere have radius a and dielectric constant K^*. Choose the line $\theta = 0$ to lie in the direction of the electric field at infinity. We assume that outside the sphere there is free space so $K = 1$ for $r > a$. The mathematical problem therefore is to solve Laplace's equation subject to the conditions:

$$V \sim -E_0 r \cos \theta \text{ as } r \to \infty,$$
$$V \text{ finite at } r = 0,$$
$$V \text{ continuous at } r = a,$$

and

$$\left(1.\frac{\partial V}{\partial r}\right)_{r=a_+}=\left(K^*\frac{\partial V}{\partial r}\right)_{r=a_-}, \tag{175}$$

where $r=a_+$ denotes a quantity evaluated at $r=a$ from a formula valid for $r>a$ and $r=a_-$ denotes a quantity evaluated at $r=a$ from a formula valid for $r<a$.

Since the boundary condition at infinity contains a factor $\cos\theta$, we try solutions for V of the form

$$V=-E_0r\cos\theta+Ar^{-2}\cos\theta \text{ for } r\geqslant a$$

and

$$V=Cr\cos\theta+Dr^{-2}\cos\theta \text{ for } r\leqslant a. \tag{176}$$

For V to be finite at $r=0$, D must be zero. For V to be continuous at $r=a$,

$$-E_0a+Aa^{-2}=Ca.$$

For equation (175) to be satisfied,

$$-E_0-2Aa^{-3}=K^*C.$$

Solving the last two equations for A and C,

$$A=a^3E_0\frac{K^*-1}{K^*+2} \text{ and } C=-E_0\frac{3}{K^*+2}.$$

Substituting back into equation (176),

$$V=-E_0\cos\theta\left(r-a^3r^{-2}\frac{K^*-1}{K^*+2}\right) \text{ for } r\geqslant a$$

and

$$V=-\frac{3}{K^*+2}E_0r\cos\theta \text{ for } r\leqslant a.$$

An arbitrary constant can be added to the expressions for V. The electric field is unaffected. This is an example of the fact, stated in chapter 1, section 1, that the scalar field, associated with an irrotational vector field is indeterminate to the extent of an arbitrary additive constant. In some problems, but not in this one, the constant is determined by the boundary conditions. Note that the electric field is uniform inside the dielectric sphere but reduced in magnitude by a factor $\frac{3}{K^*+2}$ compared to the field at infinity.

Exercise 18

Two spherical surfaces $r=a$ and $r=b$ are maintained at potentials V_a and V_b respectively. The space between the radii $r=a$ and $r=\frac{1}{2}(a+b)$ had dielectric constant K_1, that between $r=\frac{1}{2}(a+b)$ and $r=b$ has dielectric constant K_2. Find the potential at the interface $r=\frac{1}{2}(a+b)$.

Answer

$$\frac{aK_1V_a+bK_2V_b}{aK_1+bK_2}.$$

5. AXI-SYMMETRIC TEMPERATURE DISTRIBUTIONS IN A THICK HOLLOW SPHERE

Let the internal and external radii of the sphere be a and b respectively. Let $\theta=0$ be the axis of symmetry.

Case 1.

Let the temperatures of the surfaces be given by
$$T(a,\,\theta)=T_a(\theta)$$
and
$$T(b,\,\theta)=T_b(\theta).$$

FIG. 15

The problem is to find the temperature for all points whose radial co-ordinate lies between a and b.

Since T satisfies Laplace's equation and is axi-symmetric, the most general form for T, which is given by equation (170) with $m=0$, is

$$T(r, \theta) = \sum_{n=0}^{\infty} (C_n r^n + D_n r^{-n-1}) P_n(\cos \theta). \tag{179}$$

At $r = a$,

$$T(a, \theta) = \sum_{n=0}^{\infty} (C_n a^n + D_n a^{-n-1}) P_n(\cos \theta); \tag{180}$$

and at $r = b$,

$$T(b, \theta) = \sum_{n=0}^{\infty} (C_n b^n + D_n b^{-n-1}) P_n(\cos \theta). \tag{181}$$

Expand $T_a(\theta)$ and $T_b(\theta)$ in series of Legendre polynomials and equate coefficients with those in equations (180) and (181). Using equations (164) and (169)

$$T_a(\theta) = \sum_{n=0}^{\infty} A_n P_n(\cos \theta), \tag{182}$$

where

$$A_n = (n + \tfrac{1}{2}) \int_{-1}^{1} T_a(\theta) P_n(\cos \theta) \, \mathrm{d} \cos \theta$$

$$= (n + \tfrac{1}{2}) \int_{0}^{\pi} T_a(\theta) P_n(\cos \theta) \sin \theta \, \mathrm{d} \theta; \tag{183}$$

and

$$T_b(\theta) = \sum_{n=0}^{\infty} B_n P_n(\cos \theta), \tag{184}$$

where

$$B_n = (n + \tfrac{1}{2}) \int_{-1}^{1} T_b(\theta) P_n(\cos \theta) \, \mathrm{d} \cos \theta$$

$$= (n + \tfrac{1}{2}) \int_{0}^{\pi} T_b(\theta) P_n(\cos \theta) \sin \theta \, \mathrm{d} \theta. \tag{185}$$

From equations (180) and (182), $A_n = C_n a^n + D_n a^{-n-1}$; and from equations (181) and (184), $B_n = C_n b^n + D_n b^{-n-1}$. Solving for C_n and D_n,

$$C_n = \frac{A_n a^{n+1} - B_n b^{n+1}}{a^{2n+1} - b^{2n+1}} \quad \text{and} \quad D_n = \frac{A_n a^{-n} + B_n b^{-n}}{a^{-2n-1} - b^{-2n-1}}. \tag{186}$$

This completes the solution. T is given by equation (179) where the C_n and D_n are found from equations (186) and the A_n and B_n from equations (183) and (185). In most cases that occur in practice a numerical evaluation of equation (183) and (185) will be necessary.

6. FLOW PAST A NEARLY SPHERICAL BODY

A body whose surface is $r = a(1 + f(\theta, \psi))$ will be called a nearly spherical body if $f(\theta, \psi)$ is small compared to 1 for $0 \leqslant \theta \leqslant \pi$ and for $0 \leqslant \psi \leqslant 2\pi$. As a particular case consider the solid of revolution $r = a(1 + \epsilon \cos \theta)$, where ϵ^2 can be neglected compared to 1. We shall find the velocity potential of the flow of a fluid past this solid if the flow at infinity is uniform and makes angle α with the axis of revolution. The θ and ψ co-ordinates are chosen so that the radius vector from the origin parallel to the flow at infinity has equations $\theta = \alpha$, $\psi = 0$.

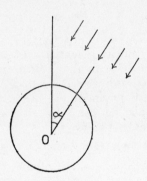

Fig. 16

The method of solution for flow past nearly spherical bodies is the same as that used in chapter 4, section 3, for a flow past a nearly cylindrical body. The solution for a flow past a sphere is modified by the addition of terms of smaller order.

The flow past a sphere can be deduced from the results of section 2 of this chapter. A uniform velocity $-U$ is superimposed on both sphere and fluid in the problem of that section so that the sphere is brought to rest and the fluid at infinity has uniform velocity $-U$. This is equivalent to adding $-Ur \cos \theta$ to the velocity potential, which will now be

$$\phi = -Ur \cos \theta (1 + \tfrac{1}{2}a^3 r^{-3}). \qquad (187)$$

This is the velocity potential when the flow at infinity is parallel to $\theta = 0$. We require the potential when the flow

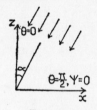

FIG. 17

is parallel to $\theta = \alpha$, $\psi = 0$. In Cartesian co-ordinates the former flow has velocity potential $-Uz$ at infinity and the latter $-U(z \cos \alpha - x \sin \alpha)$. Transforming back into spherical polar co-ordinates ($x = r \sin \theta \cos \psi$, $z = r \cos \theta$), the latter velocity potential is $-U(r \cos \theta \cos \alpha - r \sin \theta \cos \psi \sin \alpha)$. Replacing $\cos \theta$ by $\cos \theta \cos \alpha - \sin \theta \cos \psi \sin \alpha$ in equation (187) gives

$$\phi = -Ur(\cos \theta \cos \alpha - \sin \theta \cos \psi \sin \alpha)(1 + \tfrac{1}{2}a^3 r^{-3}), \quad (188)$$

which satisfies the condition at infinity. It can be verified that $\dfrac{\partial \phi}{\partial r} = 0$ at $r = a$ so that the condition at the surface of the sphere is satisfied. Since $P_1^1(\cos \theta) = \sin \theta$, equations (153), it can be verified from equations (170) that ϕ, given by equation (188), satisfies Laplace's equation. Hence equation (188) is the velocity potential for the flow past a

86

sphere when the flow at infinity is parallel to $\theta=\alpha$, $\psi=0$.

We now take equation (188) as the first approximation to the flow past the nearly spherical body

$$r=a(1+\epsilon \cos \theta). \tag{189}$$

Laplace's equation and the condition at infinity are satisfied but the condition at the body surface is violated. This latter condition is now found explicitly. Since the body is axisymmetric the normal to the surface at any point has no component in the direction ψ increasing. Let β be the angle between the direction of the normal and the direction r increasing. Then the boundary condition is (see diagram)

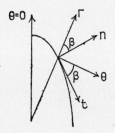

FIG. 18

$$0=v_n=v_r \cos \beta+v_\theta \sin \beta. \tag{190}$$

A small element ds along the tangent has components $r d\theta$ and $-dr$ in the θ and r directions. Hence

$$\tan \beta= -\frac{1}{r}\frac{dr}{d\theta} \quad,$$

FIG. 19

the derivatives being taken along the curve formed by the intersection of any plane ψ=constant with the body. Substituting from (189), $\tan \beta = \epsilon \sin \theta (1+\epsilon \cos \theta)^{-1}$ $= \epsilon \sin \theta + O(\epsilon^2)$. Therefore, since $\epsilon^2 \ll 1$, $\cos \beta = 1 + O(\epsilon^2)$ and $\sin \beta = \epsilon \sin \theta + O(\epsilon^2)$. Substituting for $v_r, v_\theta, \cos \beta$ and $\sin \beta$ in equation (190), the boundary condition becomes

$$\frac{\partial \phi}{\partial r} + \epsilon \sin \theta \frac{1}{r} \frac{\partial \phi}{\partial \theta} + O(\epsilon^2) = 0 \qquad (191)$$

on the surface

$$r = a (1 + \epsilon \cos \theta). \qquad (189)$$

Taylor's Theorem can be used to evaluate equation (191) at $r=a$ instead of at $r=a (1+\epsilon \cos \theta)$.

By the theorem

$$\left(\frac{\partial \phi}{\partial r}\right)_{r=a(1+\epsilon \cos \theta)} = \left(\frac{\partial \phi}{\partial r}\right)_{r=a} + a \epsilon \cos \theta \left(\frac{\partial^2 \phi}{\partial r^2}\right)_{r=a} + O(\epsilon^2)$$

and

$$\left(\frac{1}{r} \frac{\partial \phi}{\partial \theta}\right)_{r=a(1+\epsilon \cos \theta)} = \left(\frac{1}{r} \frac{\partial \phi}{\partial \theta}\right)_{r=a} + O(\epsilon).$$

Substitution in equation (191) gives the boundary condition, with error of order ϵ^2, as

$$\frac{\partial \phi}{\partial r} + \epsilon \left(a \cos \theta \frac{\partial^2 \phi}{\partial r^2} + \frac{\sin \theta}{a} \frac{\partial \phi}{\partial \theta}\right) = 0 \text{ at } r=a. \qquad (192)$$

Equation (188) is modified by the addition of a term of order ϵ, i.e. we try a velocity potential of the form

$$\phi = -Ur(\cos \theta \cos \alpha - \sin \theta \cos \psi \sin \alpha)(1 + \tfrac{1}{2}a^3r^{-3})$$
$$+ g(r, \theta, \psi) \qquad (193)$$

where g is of order ϵ. On substituting from equation (193) into equation (192), terms of zero order in ϵ vanish, terms of greater order than one in ϵ are neglected and so the two terms of order one in ϵ must be equal to zero. This gives

$$\frac{1}{\epsilon U} \left(\frac{\partial g}{\partial r}\right)_{r=a} = 3(\cos^2 \theta \cos \alpha - \sin \theta \cos \theta \cos \psi \sin \alpha)$$

$$+ \frac{3}{2}(-\sin^2 \theta \cos \alpha - \sin \theta \cos \theta \cos \psi \sin \alpha).$$

88

g must be found to satisfy this boundary condition, to vanish at infinity and to satisfy Laplace's equation. Since the functions of θ that occur in the solutions of Laplace's equation, equations (170), are Legendre polynomials and associated Legendre functions, the boundary condition is rewritten using equations (153), as

$$\frac{1}{\epsilon U}\left(\frac{\partial g}{\partial r}\right)_{r=a} = 3\cos\alpha\, P_2(\cos\theta) - \frac{3}{2}\sin\alpha\, P_2^1(\cos\theta)\cos\psi.$$
(194)

Solutions of Laplace's equation which have the forms of $P_2(\cos\theta)$ and $\cos\psi\, P_2^1(\cos\theta)$ in the variables θ and ψ and which vanish at infinity are given by equations (170) as $r^{-3}P_2(\cos\theta)$ and $r^{-3}P_2^1(\cos\theta)\cos\psi$. g is given by adding together these two solutions and by choosing the two arbitrary multiplicative constants so that equation (194) is satisfied, i.e.

$$g = -\epsilon Ua^4\cos\alpha\, r^{-3}P_2(\cos\theta) + \tfrac{1}{2}\epsilon Ua^4\sin\alpha\, r^{-3}P_2^1(\cos\theta)\cos\psi;$$

or, using equations (153),

$$g = -\tfrac{1}{4}\epsilon Ua^4\cos\alpha\, r^{-3}(3\cos2\theta+1) + \tfrac{3}{4}\epsilon Ua^4\sin\alpha\, r^{-3}\sin2\theta\cos\psi.$$
(195)

Substitute back for g from equation (195) into equation (193). This gives the velocity potential for this problem because Laplace's equation and the boundary conditions at infinity and at the surface of the body are satisfied.

Exercise 19

If the flow at infinity were parallel to the axis of revolution in the last problem, repeat the analysis in this case and verify the result by substituting $\alpha=0$ in equations (193) and (195).

Exercise 20

A nearly spherical solid of revolution has surface $r=a(1+\epsilon\cos2\theta)$. If the flow at infinity is parallel to the axis of revolution show that if ϵ^2 is neglected compared to 1, the velocity potential is given by

$$\phi = -Ur\cos\theta(1+\tfrac{1}{2}a^3r^{-3}) - \frac{3}{20}\epsilon\, Ur^{-4}a^5\,(5\cos3\theta+3\cos\theta) + \frac{9}{10}\epsilon\, Ur^{-3}a^3\cos\theta.$$

89

7. SOURCES, SINKS AND DOUBLETS

In deriving Laplace's equation for an incompressible fluid, it was assumed that the quantity of fluid in any given volume remained constant. In this section we continue to make this assumption except for volumes containing a few specified points. A point at which fluid is 'created' or added to the system is called a 'source', a point at which fluid is 'destroyed' or removed from the system is called a 'sink'. A sink is simply a negative source. The strength m of a source (or sink) is the volume flow or flux outwards (or inwards) per unit time across a small closed surface surrounding the source (or sink).

Suppose a source of strength m is situated at the origin in an otherwise undisturbed fluid medium. By symmetry the flow will be radially outwards from the origin with velocity dependent only upon the radial co-ordinate r. Consider a sphere of radius r surrounding the origin. Then equating the flow across the sphere to the strength of the source

$$4\pi r^2 v_r = m,$$

or

$$v_r = \frac{m}{4\pi r^2}.$$

By symmetry $v_\theta = v_\psi = 0$. These velocities are derivable from a velocity potential

$$\phi = -\frac{m}{4\pi r}. \tag{196}$$

Hence $-m/4\pi r$ is the velocity potential of a source of strength m. Replacing m by $-m$, the velocity potential o a sink of strength m is $m/4\pi r$. Note that $\frac{1}{r}$ satisfies Laplace's equation, see equation (170), and it vanishes at infinity.

Suppose a source and a sink each of strength m are a distance ϵ apart. Let $m \to \infty$, $\epsilon \to 0$ so that $m\epsilon$ tends to a non-zero finite limit, which we denote by μ; the resulting system is called a 'doublet' of strength μ. The line joining the source and sink is called the axis of the doublet, positive in the sense from the sink to the source. We shall now find the velocity potential of a doublet situated at the origin with axis along $\theta = 0$ and positive in the sense r increasing.

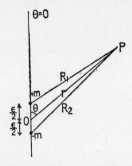

FIG. 20

Let P be any point with co-ordinates (r, θ, ψ). Then its distance R_1 from the source of strength m situated a distance $\frac{\epsilon}{2}$ from the origin along $\theta = 0$ in the positive sense is given by

$$R_1^2 = r^2 + \left(\frac{\epsilon}{2}\right)^2 - r\epsilon \cos \theta,$$

or

$$R_1 = r\left(1 - \frac{\epsilon}{r} \cos \theta + \left(\frac{\epsilon}{2r}\right)^2\right)^{\frac{1}{2}}.$$

Similarly the distance R_2 from P to the sink of strength m, situated a distance $\frac{\epsilon}{2}$ from the origin in the direction of $\theta = 0$ but in the negative sense, is

$$R_2 = r\left(1 + \frac{\epsilon}{r} \cos \theta + \left(\frac{\epsilon}{2r}\right)^2\right)^{\frac{1}{2}}.$$

91

The velocity potential at P is

$$\phi = -\frac{m}{4\pi R_1} + \frac{m}{4\pi R_2}$$

$$= -\frac{m}{4\pi r}\left\{\left(1 - \frac{\epsilon}{r}\cos\theta + \left(\frac{\epsilon}{2r}\right)^2\right)^{-\frac{1}{2}}\right.$$

$$\left. - \left(1 + \frac{\epsilon}{r}\cos\theta + \left(\frac{\epsilon}{2r}\right)^2\right)^{-\frac{1}{2}}\right\}$$

$$= -\frac{m\epsilon\cos\theta}{4\pi r^2} + m\epsilon O(\epsilon).$$

Let $m \to \infty$, $\epsilon \to 0$ such that $m\epsilon \to \mu$, then in the limit

$$\phi = -\frac{\mu\cos\theta}{4\pi r^2}. \tag{197}$$

Hence $-\dfrac{\mu\cos\theta}{4\pi r^2}$ is the velocity potential of a doublet of strength μ, where θ is the angle between the axis of the doublet and the line joining it to the point at which the velocity potential is required. Again note that $\cos\theta/r^2$ satisfies Laplace's equation and vanishes at infinity.

If the velocity potential found in section 2 of this chapter is compared with equation (197), it can be seen that the velocity field outside a sphere moving with velocity U is the same as that due to a doublet of strength $\mu = 2\pi a^3 U$ instantaneously placed at the centre of the sphere.

Sources and sinks of heat and doublets can be introduced into the theory of heat conduction in a manner similar to that employed above for fluid flow. The electrostatic analogies are positive and negative point charges and doublets. Doublets can only be introduced into gravitational theory if the concept of negative mass is admitted. The factor 4π is not included in the denominators of equations (196) and (197) in electrostatic theory. Just as a source and a sink were combined to produce a doublet so two doublets of equal strength, direction but opposite sense, can be combined to produce a 'quadrupole', and so on.

8. DOUBLET IN A FLUID BOUNDED BY A SPHERE

A doublet of strength μ is situated at the centre of a hollow sphere of radius a enclosing fluid. Find the velocity field in the fluid.

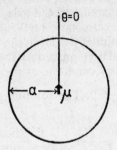

FIG. 21

Take $\theta = 0$ along the axis of the doublet and in the same sense. The velocity potential, equation (197), accounts for the presence of the doublet and satisfies Laplace's equation but it does not satisfy the boundary condition $v_r = \dfrac{\partial \phi}{\partial r} = 0$ at the surface of the sphere $r = a$.

Other terms must be added to this velocity potential to satisfy the boundary condition. These terms must satisfy Laplace's equation and must be continuous at the origin since the discontinuity (the doublet) at that point is already accounted for by the first term. Examination of equations (170) show that there is only one such term, whose dependence on θ is proportional to $\cos \theta$ and which is independent of ψ, namely $r \cos \theta$. We therefore try

$$\phi = -\frac{\mu \cos \theta}{4\pi r^2} + Ar \cos \theta$$

where A is constant. $\dfrac{\partial \phi}{\partial r} = 0$ at $r = a$ if $A = -\dfrac{\mu}{2\pi a^3}$. The

93

velocity potential is

$$\phi = -\frac{\mu \cos \theta}{4\pi r^2}\left(1 + \frac{2r^3}{a^3}\right). \tag{198}$$

Since $r \cos \theta$ is the velocity potential for a uniform flow parallel to $\theta = 0$, the flow inside the sphere is the superposition of the flow due to a doublet in an infinite fluid and of a uniform flow parallel to the axis of the doublet.

The analogous electrostatic (or heat conduction) problem is that of a doublet placed at the centre of a spherical shell made of insulating material. If the shell were conducting the boundary condition at $r = a$ would be $\phi = $ constant instead of $\frac{\partial \phi}{\partial r} = 0$. The solution gives the field inside the shell.

Note that equation (198) is identical to equation (197) if $\mu = 2\pi a^3 U$. But the identity is purely formal because equation (198) represents flow inside the sphere whereas equation (187) represents flow outside the sphere.

Exercise 21

An electrostatic doublet of strength μ is placed at the centre of a hollow earthed conducting sphere of radius a. Find the potential inside the sphere.

Answer

$$V = \mu \cos \theta \left(\frac{1}{r^2} - \frac{r}{a^3}\right).$$

9. DOUBLET IN A CAVITY IN A DIELECTRIC MEDIUM

The electrostatic potential due to a point charge $+\rho$ situated at the origin is $V = \rho/r$. By a method identical to that used for fluid doublets in section 7, it can be shown that the potential due to a doublet of strength μ situated at the origin with its axis parallel to $\theta = 0$ and positive in the sense of r increasing is

$$V = \frac{\mu \cos \theta}{r^2}. \tag{199}$$

94

If the doublet is placed at the centre of a spherical cavity of radius a in an infinite dielectric of constant K, then the potential V must satisfy the following conditions:

(i) Laplace's equation must be satisfied everywhere;

(ii) Apart from the term $\dfrac{\mu \cos \theta}{r^2}$, V must be continuous at the origin,

(iii) V must be continuous at $r = a$,

(iv) $\left(\dfrac{\partial V}{\partial r}\right)_{r=a_-} = K\left(\dfrac{\partial V}{\partial r}\right)_{r=a_+}$, see equation (175),

and

(v) V must tend to zero as $r \to \infty$.

To satisfy conditions (i) and (ii), try as potential inside the cavity

$$V = \frac{\mu \cos \theta}{r^2} + Ar \cos \theta, \quad r < a; \tag{200}$$

and to satisfy conditions (i) and (v), try as potential outside the cavity

$$V = B\frac{\cos \theta}{r^2}. \tag{201}$$

These potentials are correct if the constants A and B can be chosen to satisfy conditions (iii) and (iv). To satisfy condition (iii)

$$\frac{\mu \cos \theta}{a^2} + Aa \cos \theta = B\frac{\cos \theta}{a^2},$$

and to satisfy condition (iv)

$$-\frac{2\mu \cos \theta}{a^3} + A \cos \theta = -2BK\frac{\cos \theta}{a^3}.$$

Solving the last two equations

$$A = \frac{2\mu(1-K)}{a^3(1+2K)} \text{ and } B = \frac{3\mu}{1+2K}. \tag{202}$$

95

Substitution back into equations (200) and (201) gives the required electrostatic potentials.

Exercise 22

A point charge ρ is placed at the centre of a spherical cavity of radius a in an infinite dielectric medium of constant K. Find the potential everywhere, assuming that it tends to zero at infinity.

Answer

$$V = \begin{cases} \dfrac{\rho}{r} - \dfrac{K-1}{K}\dfrac{\rho}{a}, & r \leqslant a \\[2mm] \dfrac{\rho}{Kr}, & r \geqslant a. \end{cases}$$